Contents

How to use this book	2
Rounding	3–5
Making 1 and 10	6
Doubling and halving	7
Doubling and halving problems	8
Multiplying and dividing	9–10
Multiplying and dividing problems	11
Equivalent fractions	12–13
Adding	14
Subtracting	15
Adding and subtracting	16
Factors and primes	17–18
Multiplying and dividing by 10, 100 and 1000	19
Multiplying and dividing by 0·1 and 0·01	20
Multiplying fractions	21–22
Fractions problems	23
Dividing	24–26
Decimal numbers	27
Adding and subtracting decimals	28–29
Adding decimals	30–31
Subtracting decimals	32–33
Decimal problems	34, 43
Powers and prime factors	35
Powers	36
Positive and negative numbers	37
Adding and subtracting negative numbers	38
Multiplying decimals	39–40
Dividing decimals	41–42
Calculating percentages	44–46
Fractions and percentages	47
Fractions, decimals and percentages	48
Proportion	49
Ratio	50
Checking calculations	51–52
Square numbers and cube numbers	53
Square roots and cube roots	54
Squares, cubes and roots	55
Using brackets	56
Calculations with brackets	57
Using letters	58–61
Combining terms	62–63
Substituting	64, 66
Brackets	65
Formulae	67–68
Finding formulae	69
Equations	70–71
Arithmogons	72
Straight-line graphs	73–75
Graphs	76–78
Function machines	79–81
Sequences	82–84
The nth term	85–87
Weight and capacity	88–89
Weight and capacity problems	90
Surface area	91–93
Area	94–95
Area problems	96
Lines and angles	97
Angles of a triangle	98
Coordinates	99–100
Drawing reflections	101–102
Rotating shapes	103
Rotations, reflections, transformations	104
Order of rotational symmetry	105
Line symmetry and rotational symmetry	106
Views of 3-d shapes	107–108
Congruent shapes	109
2-d shapes	110
Constructing triangles	111
Constructing triangles and quadrilaterals	112
Representing data	113–114
Interpreting graphs	115
Mean, median, mode	116
Averages and spread	117
Averages problems	118
Probability	119–120
Probability problems	121
Mixed problems	122–128

How to use this book

Each page has a title telling you what it is about.

Instructions look like this. Always read these carefully before starting.

Ask your teacher if you need to do these.

Sometimes the first question is done for you to show you the method to use.

This shows that the activity is an **Explore**. Take time to investigate the question. Write as many answers as you can.

This means you decide how to set out your work.

Read these word problems very carefully. Decide how you will work out the answers.

Sometimes there is a **Hint** to help you.

$$A = lw$$
$$P = 2(l + w)$$

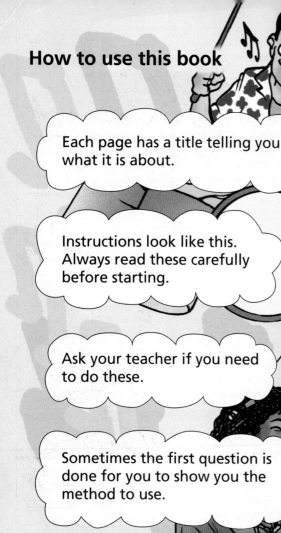

Rounding

Write the position of each pointer. Round the number to its nearest 1 decimal place.

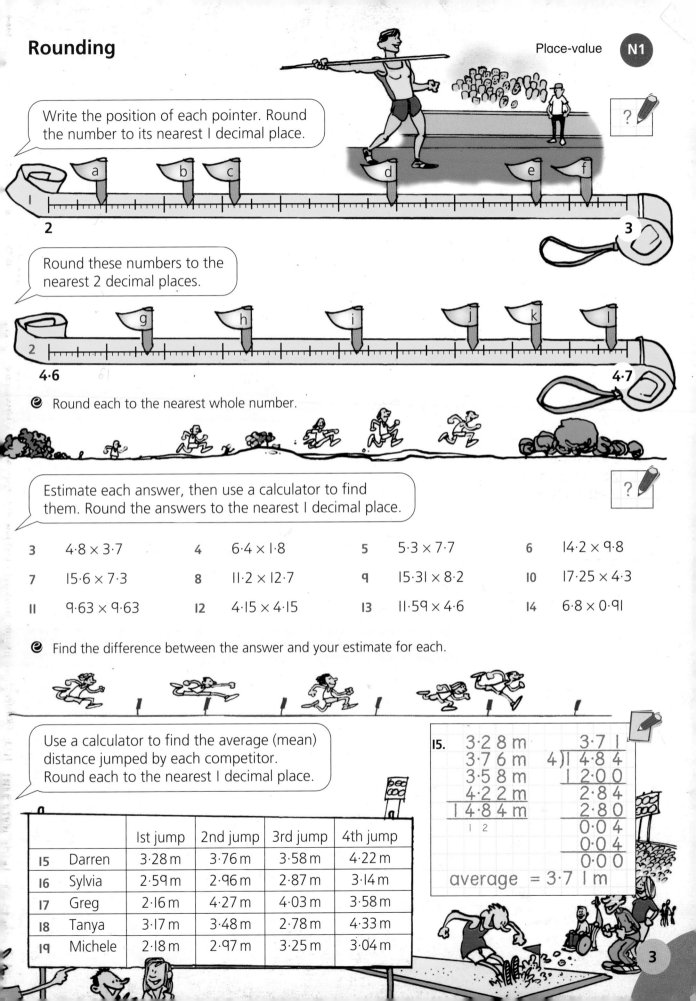

a b c d e f

2 3

Round these numbers to the nearest 2 decimal places.

g h i j k l

2

4·6 61 4·7

⊘ Round each to the nearest whole number.

Estimate each answer, then use a calculator to find them. Round the answers to the nearest 1 decimal place.

3	$4\cdot8 \times 3\cdot7$	4	$6\cdot4 \times 1\cdot8$	5	$5\cdot3 \times 7\cdot7$	6	$14\cdot2 \times 9\cdot8$
7	$15\cdot6 \times 7\cdot3$	8	$11\cdot2 \times 12\cdot7$	9	$15\cdot31 \times 8\cdot2$	10	$17\cdot25 \times 4\cdot3$
11	$9\cdot63 \times 9\cdot63$	12	$4\cdot15 \times 4\cdot15$	13	$11\cdot59 \times 4\cdot6$	14	$6\cdot8 \times 0\cdot91$

⊘ Find the difference between the answer and your estimate for each.

Use a calculator to find the average (mean) distance jumped by each competitor.
Round each to the nearest 1 decimal place.

15.
```
 3·2 8 m          3·7 1
 3·7 6 m      4 )1 4·8 4
 3·5 8 m        1 2·0 0
 4·2 2 m          2·8 4
1 4·8 4 m         2·8 0
   1 2            0·0 4
                  0·0 4
                  0·0 0
average = 3·7 1 m
```

		1st jump	2nd jump	3rd jump	4th jump
15	Darren	3·28 m	3·76 m	3·58 m	4·22 m
16	Sylvia	2·59 m	2·96 m	2·87 m	3·14 m
17	Greg	2·16 m	4·27 m	4·03 m	3·58 m
18	Tanya	3·17 m	3·48 m	2·78 m	4·33 m
19	Michele	2·18 m	2·97 m	3·25 m	3·04 m

3

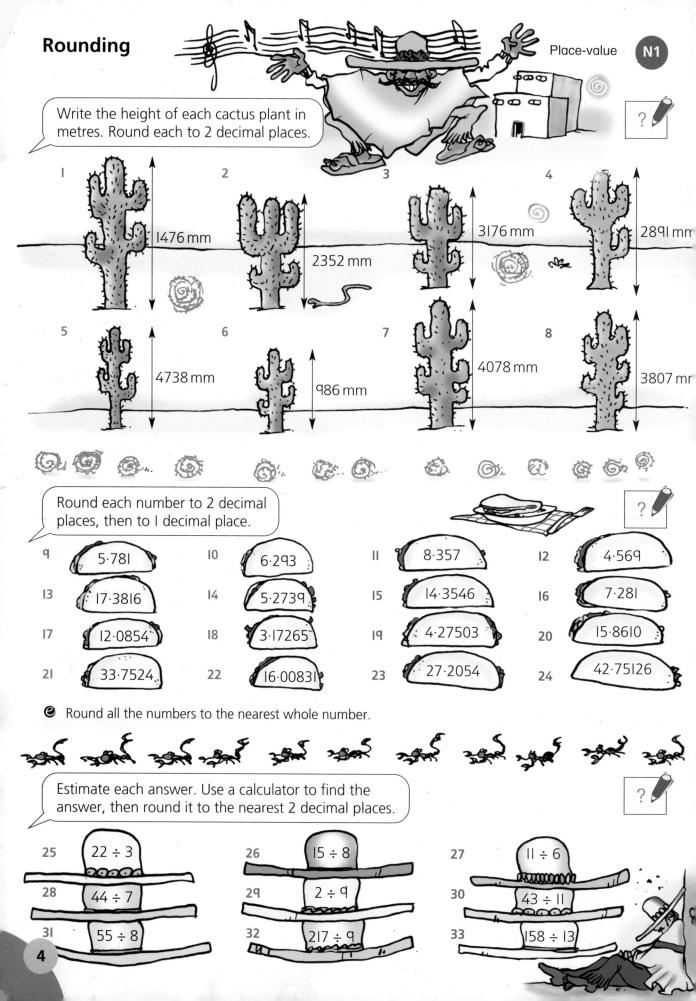

Write the height of each cactus plant in metres. Round each to 2 decimal places.

1 1476 mm

2 2352 mm

3 3176 mm

4 2891 mm

5 4738 mm

6 986 mm

7 4078 mm

8 3807 mm

Round each number to 2 decimal places, then to 1 decimal place.

9   5·781

10 6·293

11 8·357

12 4·569

13 17·3816

14 5·2739

15 14·3546

16 7·281

17 12·0854

18 3·17265

19 4·27503

20 15·8610

21 33·7524

22 16·00831

23 27·2054

24 42·75126

ℓ Round all the numbers to the nearest whole number.

Estimate each answer. Use a calculator to find the answer, then round it to the nearest 2 decimal places.

25 22 ÷ 3

26 15 ÷ 8

27 11 ÷ 6

28 44 ÷ 7

29 2 ÷ 9

30 43 ÷ 11

31 55 ÷ 8

32 217 ÷ 9

33 158 ÷ 13

Rounding

Give an approximate answer to each of these questions.

1 A concert is attended by 2320 people on the first night and 3789 people on the second night. How many people to the nearest hundred attended over the two days?

2. A group of 20 friends buys tickets to the concert. They spend £596 on tickets. How much to the nearest pound do they each spend?

Problems

3 Selina is flying from Singapore to London. The journey takes $12\frac{1}{2}$ hours. She has been travelling for 380 minutes so far. Approximately how many more hours of the journey are left?

4 The return air fare from London to Singapore costs £489. If it decreases by 10%, roughly how much will Selina save?

5 A recipe needs 75 g of flour to make 5 cup cakes. Approximately how many kilograms are needed to make 150 cup cakes?

6 The cup cakes are sold at the school fête for 19p each. If all 150 cakes are sold, approximately how much money is taken?

Explore

Use a stopwatch which records hundredths of a second.

Close your eyes, start the watch and stop it when you think 10 seconds have passed. Record the time, e.g. 8·71 seconds.

Reset the watch and repeat two more times.

Find the average (mean) time and round it to the nearest 1 decimal place.

Repeat for estimating other times, e.g. 30 seconds, 60 seconds, 45 seconds.

Making 1 and 10

Each metre stick has been chopped in two.
Write the length of the other piece in metres.

1 0·3 m

2 0·76 m

3 0·24 m

4 0·16 m

5 0·40 m

6 0·38 m

7 48 cm

8 27 cm

9 370 mm

Write how much has been spent from a
£10 note to give each amount of change.

10 £7·36

11 £8·15

12 £0·72

13 £5·50

14 £4·63

15 £1·98

16 £7·09

17 £6·27

18 £2·03

19 £6·88

20 £0·84

21 £9·21

Write how much has been drunk
from each litre bottle in litres.

22 0·735 l

23 0·526 l

24 0·418 l

25 0·925 l

26 275 ml

27 38 cl

28 158 ml

29 0·805 l

30 0·075 l

🄮 Estimate how much has been drunk in pints.

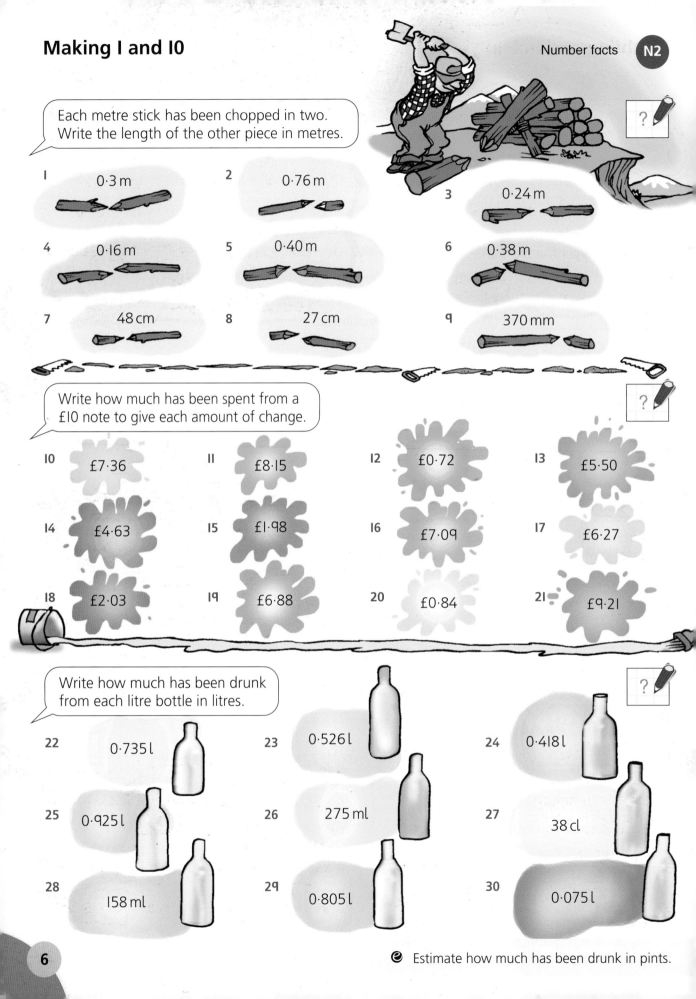

Doubling and halving

Write the doubles of these numbers.

I	26	2	4·7	3	0·35	4	2·8	5	37
6	0·58	7	7·7	8	59	9	0·18	10	6·7
II	74	12	0·29	13	9·3	14	0·47	15	0·86

The length of each snake doubles in one year. Write the lengths next year.

16	0·76 m	17	0·39 m	18	0·47 m	19	0·28 m
20	0·93 m	21	0·67 m	22	0·58 m	23	0·37 m

ℯ How many years before each snake is over 5 m long?

Simran travels these distances, there and back, from home. Write how far away each place is from home.

24	7·6 km	25	5·6 km	26	15·8 km
27	3·2 km	28	17·0 km	29	19·4 km
30	13·8 km	31	9·2 km	32	11·4 km

ℯ Write how far away each place is in miles.

Each item is reduced to half-price. Write the new prices.

33	£8·96	34	£13·78	35	£12·46	36	£15·48
37	£4·38	38	£5·78	39	£16·98	40	£11·38

ℯ Write double each price.

Doubling and halving problems

Pizza Prices

Margherita	£4·60
Napoletana	£4·85
Mushroom	£4·70
Pepperoni	£6·45
Hawaiian	£5·80
Four Seasons	£6·65

1　Carla buys 2 pepperoni pizzas. Find the cost.

2　Louis buys a Napoletana. How much change does he get from £10?

3　Sanjay buys 2 mushroom pizzas. How much change does he get from £20?

4　To buy 2 pizzas of the same type Ellie spends £11·60. Which type of pizza has she chosen?

5　David buys 4 pizzas. It costs £22·45. He buys a mushroom pizza and 2 pepperoni pizzas. Which other pizza does he buy?

6　The pizza place has a special 'buy one pizza get another half price' offer. Martin buys 2 mushroom pizzas and 2 Hawaiian pizzas. How much does he spend?

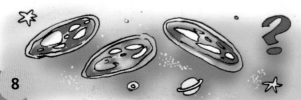

Multiplying and dividing

Use factors to find the areas of these gardens.

I. $4.5 \times 2 = 9$
$9 \times 8 = 72$
$4.5\,m \times 16\,m = 72\,m^2$

I 16 m
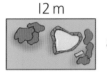 4.5 m

2 18 m
5.3 m

3 14 m
6.1 m

4 12 m
8.3 m

5 36 m
3.25 m

6 32 m
9.25 m

Check each calculation using partitioning.

Ia. $4.5 \times 16 = (4.5 \times 10) + (4.5 \times 6)$
$= 45 + 27 = 72$

Use factors to find the heights of these buildings. A is the area of the front wall.

7. $138 \div 2 = 69$
$69 \div 3 = 23$
$138\,m^2 \div 6\,m = 23\,m$

7
A = 138 m²
6 m

8
A = 372 m²
12 m

9
A = 345 m²
15 m

10
A = 378 m²
18 m

11
A = 432 m²
16 m

12
A = 490 m²
14 m

Use partitioning to complete these divisions.

I3. $100 \div 9 = 11\ r\ 1$
$76 \div 9 = 8\ r\ 4$
$176 \div 9 = 19\ r\ 5$

13	176 ÷ 9	**14**	126 ÷ 8	**15**	234 ÷ 6
16	184 ÷ 15	**17**	223 ÷ 13	**18**	312 ÷ 12
19	516 ÷ 21	**20**	231 ÷ 18	**21**	335 ÷ 11

Multiplying and dividing

Use doubling and halving to find the areas of these posters.

I. $43m \times 16m = 86 \times 8 = 172 \times 4$
$= 344 \times 2 = 688m^2$

1	43 cm

16 cm

| 2 | 23 cm |

18 cm

| 3 | 33 cm |

14 cm

| 4 | 37·5 cm |

22 cm

| 5 | 46·5 cm |

12 cm

| 6 | 18 cm |

6·5 cm

℮ Write the perimeter of each poster.

Copy and complete the table by doubling.
Use the table to complete the calculations.

2·37	×1	=
2·37	×2	=
2·37	×4	=
2·37	×8	=
2·37	×16	=

7 $2·37 \times 9$ 8 $2·37 \times 17$

9 $2·37 \times 12$ 10 $2·37 \times 7$

11 $2·37 \times 14$ 12 $2·37 \times 31$

Use doubling tables to solve these problems.

Bricks weigh 3·24 kg. Write the weight of:
13   14   15

Planks weigh 5·32 kg. Write the weight of:
16   17   18

7 bricks   15 bricks   13 bricks   5 planks   18 planks   25 planks

Complete these multiplications using four different methods.

19 using factors   20 partitioning

21 doubling and halving   22 using a doubling table

18×26

$2·45 \times 12$

$3·65 \times 18$

Multiplying and dividing problems

Solve these problems.
Explain the method you use.

1 In a tennis tournament 16 tennis balls are used in each match. How many balls are used in 32 matches?

2 Programmes cost £1·80 at a football match. 2350 people attend. How much is spent on programmes if half the people buy one?

3 There are 5200 people at a concert. They sit in rows of 26 people. How many complete rows do they take up?

4 A ticket agent takes £5167·50 on tickets that cost £32·50 each. How many tickets does he sell?

5 Steve spends £15·50 on 6 colas and 4 hot dogs. If a cola costs £1·35, how much is a hot dog?

6 An 8-man boat crew weighs a total of 842 kg. What is their average mass?

7 A football strip (shirt and shorts) costs £46·50. The team spends £558 on a strip for 12 players. If the 12 shirts come to £294, how much does a pair of shorts cost?

8 In a motor race the winning car travels 231 miles in 2 hours 45 minutes. What is its average speed in miles per hour?

Equivalent fractions

Complete these pairs of equivalent fractions.

1 $\frac{3}{4} = \frac{\square}{8}$

2 $\frac{4}{5} = \frac{\square}{20}$

3 $\frac{2}{3} = \frac{\square}{12}$

4 $\frac{2}{\square} = \frac{1}{3}$

5 $\frac{\square}{8} = \frac{3}{4}$

6 $\frac{1}{4} = \frac{2}{\square}$

7 $\frac{\square}{10} = \frac{4}{5}$

8 $\frac{5}{12} = \frac{25}{\square}$

9 $\frac{7}{15} = \frac{\square}{30}$

10 $\frac{\square}{9} = \frac{14}{18}$

11 $\frac{17}{20} = \frac{\square}{100}$

12 $\frac{\square}{25} = \frac{76}{100}$

Simplify these fractions by cancelling.

13 $\frac{4}{6}$

14 $\frac{8}{12}$

15 $\frac{12}{18}$

16 $\frac{12}{16}$

17 $\frac{20}{30}$

18 $\frac{9}{15}$

19 $\frac{7}{21}$

20 $\frac{8}{20}$

21 $\frac{24}{30}$

22 $\frac{2}{18}$

23 $\frac{16}{20}$

24 $\frac{6}{18}$

25 $\frac{21}{28}$

26 $\frac{12}{36}$

27 $\frac{20}{25}$

28 $\frac{6}{15}$

29 $\frac{35}{50}$

30 $\frac{28}{36}$

31 $\frac{72}{81}$

32 $\frac{85}{100}$

e Write each row of five fractions in order of size.

Write each pair of fractions with the same denominator. Write them in order using the '<' sign.

33. $\frac{2}{5} = \frac{4}{10}$

$\frac{3}{10} < \frac{4}{10}$

$\frac{3}{10} < \frac{2}{5}$

33 $\frac{2}{5}$ 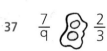 $\frac{3}{10}$

34 $\frac{5}{6}$  $\frac{2}{3}$

35 $\frac{3}{4}$ $\frac{5}{8}$

36 $\frac{1}{2}$  $\frac{5}{6}$

37 $\frac{7}{9}$ 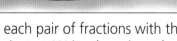 $\frac{2}{3}$

38 $\frac{5}{7}$ $\frac{11}{14}$

39 $\frac{3}{4}$ $\frac{2}{3}$

40 $\frac{1}{2}$ $\frac{3}{5}$

41 $\frac{1}{2}$ $\frac{2}{3}$

42 $\frac{3}{4}$ $\frac{4}{5}$

43 $\frac{2}{3}$  $\frac{7}{10}$

44 $\frac{31}{50}$ $\frac{63}{100}$

Equivalent fractions

Find the lowest common denominator for each set of fractions. Write equivalent fractions to match.

I. $\frac{1}{4} = \frac{2}{8}$

$\frac{1}{2} = \frac{4}{8}$

$\frac{2}{8}, \frac{3}{8}, \frac{4}{8}$

1 $\frac{1}{4}, \frac{1}{2}, \frac{3}{8}$

2 $\frac{1}{3}, \frac{1}{2}, \frac{5}{6}$

3 $\frac{3}{5}, \frac{1}{2}, \frac{7}{10}$

4 $\frac{1}{3}, \frac{1}{4}, \frac{5}{12}$

5 $\frac{5}{6}, \frac{11}{12}, \frac{3}{4}$

6 $\frac{2}{3}, \frac{1}{2}, \frac{7}{12}$

7 $\frac{3}{5}, \frac{2}{3}, \frac{11}{15}$

8 $\frac{1}{3}, \frac{3}{8}, \frac{1}{4}$

9 $\frac{2}{3}, \frac{5}{6}, \frac{1}{4}$

10 $\frac{9}{20}, \frac{2}{5}, \frac{1}{4}$

11 $\frac{2}{3}, \frac{3}{4}, \frac{4}{5}$

12 $\frac{2}{3}, \frac{1}{2}, \frac{3}{5}$

13 $\frac{1}{3}, \frac{2}{5}, \frac{5}{6}$

14 $\frac{11}{20}, \frac{3}{5}, \frac{19}{25}$

15 $\frac{4}{5}, \frac{7}{8}, \frac{17}{20}$

Find the difference between the largest and smallest fractions in each set. Simplify the answer.

16 Karen spent $\frac{1}{3}$ of her savings, and then another $\frac{1}{4}$. What fraction of her savings does she have left?

17 In a vote for class sports' captain, $\frac{1}{3}$ of the children voted for Jenny, and $\frac{1}{6}$ voted for Kim. What fraction of the class did not vote for either?

Problems

18 Last weekend, Rajesh read $\frac{3}{8}$ of his book. The weekend before he read $\frac{1}{4}$ of it. What fraction of the book is still left to read?

19 If you spend $\frac{1}{2}$ of the day sleeping, $\frac{1}{3}$ at school, and $\frac{1}{8}$ eating, what fraction of the day is left?

 **Explore**

Make 10 additions of two fractions, each having a different denominator. Show why each addition is correct.

Write some additions of three fractions.

Adding

Write three calculations to find the total weight for each pair. Add by doubling first and use a different double each time.

I. 9·4 kg
Ia. double 4·6 + 0·2
Ib. double 4·8 − 0·2
Ic. double 5 − 0·4 − 0·2

I 4·6 kg 4·8 kg

2 6·7 kg 6·4 kg

3 8·7 kg 8·9 kg

4 5·36 kg 5·38 kg

5 6·69 kg 6·72 kg

6 8·54 kg 8·51 kg

Write the total capacity for each pair by adding parts in turn (partitioning).

7.

8·0

0·3

4·9   1 2·9   1 3·2

4·9 l + 8·3 l = 1 3·2 l

7 4·9 l 8·3 l

8 5·74 l 2·6 l

9 7·57 l 4·6 l

10 3·27 l 1·46 l

11 5·83 l 2·43 l

12 7·28 l 2·83 l

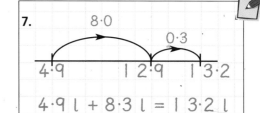

Check three of your answers by subtracting one of the numbers from the answer.

Write the total distance for each pair by adding too much, then adjusting (compensating).

13.

3·0

0·1

7·3   1 0·2   1 0·3

7·3 km + 2·9 km = 1 0·2 km

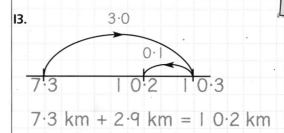

13 7·3 km 2·9 km

14 8·63 km 4·8 km

15 6·29 km 3·7 km

16 5·35 km 1·95 km

17 4·28 km 3·87 km

18 19·36 km 2·78 km

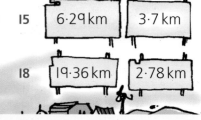

e Check your answers using subtraction.

Subtracting

> Write the difference between the times in each pair. Subtract by finding the difference.

I.
3·3
0·2
4·8   5·0   8·3
8·3 s − 4·8 s = 3·5 s

1   8·3 s   4·8 s

2   6·5 s   2·7 s

3   3·8 s   6·52 s

4   5·3 s   11·73 s

5   2·84 s   6·59 s

6   13·96 s   19·49 s

> Find the length of material left on each roll by subtracting parts in turn (partitioning).

7.
4·0
0·7
4·7   5·4   9·4
9·4 m − 4·7 m = 4·7 m

7   9·4 m cut off 4·7 m

8   11·3 m cut off 6·6 m

9   14·35 m cut off 6·8 m

10   8·34 m cut off 2·8 m

11   15·29 m cut off 6·77 m

12   4·78 m cut off 1·34 m

ℯ Check three of your answers by adding your answer to the amount cut off.

7a.
5·0
0·3
4·4   4·7   9·4
9·4 m − 4·7 m = 4·7 m

> Repeat to find the answers by subtracting too much, then adjusting (compensating).

Problems

13   When I am added to 3·8, the total is 9·7. What number am I?

14   I am 1·56 more than 4·65. What number am I?

15   When my double is added to 0·15 the result is 7·45. What number am I?

16   I am 2·9 less than 7·81. What number am I?

17   I am more than 4. I differ from 3·8 by 1·85. What number am I?

18   I am half the difference between 9·82 and 12·66. What number am I?

15

Adding and subtracting

Write how tall each tree is now.

1   3·45 m
    1·7 m cut off

2   4·67 m
    grows 0·82 m

3   5·4 m
    0·65 m cut off

4   4·08 m
    3·9 m cut off

5   3·97 m
    grows 0·46 m

6   3·6 m
    grows 1·99 m

Robbie saves his coins in bottles. Write how much money he has left in each bottle if he buys these items with each type of coin.

7   2980
    1p coins

8   845
    2p coins

9   434
    5p coins

a   £15·99

b   £6·75

c   £11·49

d   £0·95

Factors and primes

Write a possible missing digit for each number.

I. 2 3 2 4 7, 2 3 5 4 7, or 2 3 8 4 7

1	23 ✱ 47	divisible by 3
2	52 ✱ 6	divisible by 9
3	2756 ✱	divisible by 5
4	1526 ✱	divisible by 4
5	37 ✱	divisible by 4
6	53267 ✱	divisible by 2
7	27 ✱ 196	divisible by 3
8	706 ✱	divisible by 7
9	2 ✱ 2	divisible by 8
10	47 ✱	divisible by 6

Make a list of the pairs of factors of each number. Try dividing each by 2, by 3, by 4, ...

11	82	12	75	13	108	14	145
15	188	16	221	17	103	18	94

Write all the common factors for each pair of numbers.

19	8 and 10	20	12 and 20	21	45 and 30
22	24 and 32	23	16 and 18	24	72 and 48
25	50 and 40	26	36 and 63	27	49 and 42

Explore

Choose any number, e.g. 12.

Write different numbers which add up to make your chosen number, then multiply them together. E.g.

2 + 10 = 12 → 2 × 10 = 20

Explore which set of numbers will give the greatest product.

Repeat for different starting numbers.

Factors and primes

Write the next prime number after each of these numbers.

1 22

2 33

3 7

4 16

5 9

6 41

7 18

8 57

9 40

10 70

11 90

12 100

Draw a factor tree for each of these numbers.
Write each number as the product of its prime factors.

13 270

14 1690

15 976

16 837

17 2500

18 2662

19 4332

20 30 030

Problems

21 I am a factor of 32 and I am a square number. I am an even number. Who am I?

22 I am a factor of 20 and a factor of 48. I am more than 2. Who am I?

23 I am the highest factor of 45, except for 45. Who am I?

24 I am the only even prime number. Who am I?

25 I am a number less than 10. The total of my factors is 12. Who am I?

26 I am the only odd number between 10 and 21 which is not prime. Who am I?

27 I am a number between 10 and 20. The total of my factors is 31. Who am I?

28 I am a prime number between 20 and 50. I am the next number after a square number. Who am I?

29 I am the ninth prime number. Who am I?

30 I am a prime number found by subtracting a square number from 100. Who am I?

Explore

5 and 7 are consecutive odd numbers.

They are both prime.

Explore other pairs of consecutive odd numbers which are both prime.

odd numbers
1, 3, 5, 7, 9, ...

prime numbers
1, 2, 3, 5, 7, ...

Copy and complete.

1 $10 \times 0.4 =$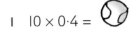

2 $5.7 \div 10 =$

3 $0.8 \times 10 =$

4 $10 \times 4.6 =$

5 $100 \times 3.25 =$

6 $10 \times 7.68 =$

7 $4.32 \div 10 =$

8 $4.57 \times 1000 =$

9 $28.6 \div 10 =$

10 $1.8 \div 100 =$

11 $6 \div 10 =$

12 $2.79 \times 10 =$

13 $39.4 \div 1000 =$

14 $1000 \times 2.71 =$

15 $18 \div 1000 =$

16 $10 \times 43.7 =$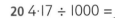

17 $472 \div 100 =$

18 $39.4 \div 10 =$

19 $9.01 \times 10 =$

20 $4.17 \div 1000 =$

Write the missing numbers.

21 $28.7 \times$  $= 287$

22 $31.6 \div$ $= 0.316$

23 $456 \div$ $= 0.456$

24 $4.38 \times$ $= 43.8$

25 $7.65 \div$ $= 0.765$

26 $0.83 \times$ $= 830$

27 $1.93 \times$  $= 193$

28 $71.5 \div$  $= 0.0715$

29 $27.6 \div$ $= 2.76$

30 $8.72 \div$ $= 0.0872$

31 $0.35 \times$  $= 35$

32 $5.46 \times$ = 5460

🍴 Which multiple of 10 must each number be multiplied or divided by to make an answer between 1 and 10?

Problems

33 The weight of 1000 marbles is 2·47 kg. How much does each marble weigh?

34 The cost of 10 footballs is £57·60. How much change will there be from £10 when buying 1 football?

35 An athlete runs 100 laps of a field, making a total distance of 38·6 km. How far is it around the field in metres?

19

Multiplying and dividing by 0·1 and 0·01

Copy and complete.

1	$5·2 \times 0·1$	2	$8·6 \div 0·1$	3	$2·3 \times 0·01$
4	$56·7 \times 0·01$	5	$2·3 \div 0·01$	6	$11 \div 0·1$
7	$72·3 \div 0·1$	8	$7 \times 0·1$	9	$15·7 \div 0·01$
10	$138 \times 0·01$	11	$0·83 \div 0·01$	12	$8·35 \times 0·1$
13	$46·7 \times 0·1$	14	$432 \div 0·1$	15	$9·62 \div 0·01$
16	$5·64 \div 0·1$	17	$4 \times 0·01$	18	$10 \div 0·01$

Write the missing numbers.

19 $5·6 \times$ 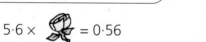 $= 0·56$

20 $7·83 \times$  $= 0·0783$

21 $8·3 \div$ ❦ $= 83$

22 $56·2 \times$ ✿ $= 0·562$

23 $42·8 \div$ 🦋 $= 4280$

24 $2·7 \times$ ❦ $= 0·027$

25 $19·4 \div$ 🍃 $= 194$

26 $143 \times$ 🦋 $= 1·43$

27 $396 \div$ ✿ $= 39\,600$

28 $0·28 \div$ ❦ $= 28·0$

Write true or false for each.

29 $0·4 \div 10 = 400 \times 0·01$

30 $1·7 \times 0·1 = 0·017 \div 0·1$

31 $5·62 \div 0·01 = 5620 \times 0·1$

32 $38·3 \times 0·01 = 3·83 \div 0·1$

33 $174 \div 0·1 = 174\,000 \times 0·01$

34 $14·71 \times 0·1 = 1·471 \times 10$

35 $96·8 \div 0·01 = 9·68 \times 1000$

36 $4030 \times 0·01 = 4·03 \times 100$

37 $127·51 \div 100 = 0·12751 \div 0·1$

38 $0·043 \times 1000 = 0·43 \div 0·01$

Multiplying fractions

Write the fraction of each amount.

I. $\frac{2}{3}$ of £24 = £16

£24 | 1 $\frac{2}{3}$ | 2 $\frac{3}{4}$ | 3 $\frac{5}{6}$ | 4 $\frac{7}{8}$

£20 | 5 $\frac{7}{10}$ | 6 $\frac{3}{5}$ | 7 $\frac{3}{4}$ | 8 $\frac{6}{5}$

£36 | 9 $\frac{2}{3}$ | 10 $\frac{5}{6}$ | 11 $\frac{3}{4}$ | 12 $\frac{7}{12}$

£30 | 13 $\frac{3}{5}$ | 14 $\frac{2}{3}$ | 15 $\frac{5}{6}$ | 16 $\frac{4}{15}$

FIRST FLOOR

Copy and complete.

17 $\frac{2}{3} \times 12$

18 $\frac{3}{4} \times 8$

19 $\frac{4}{5} \times 20$

20 $\frac{5}{6} \times 18$

21 $\frac{3}{7} \times 14$

22 $\frac{5}{8} \times 24$

23 $15 \times \frac{3}{5}$

24 $16 \times \frac{3}{8}$

25 $30 \times \frac{7}{10}$

26 $18 \times \frac{7}{9}$

27 $21 \times \frac{5}{7}$

28 $9 \times \frac{1}{6}$

GROUND FLOOR

Write the missing fractions.

29  $\times 24 = 8$

30 $\times 40 = 20$

31 $\times 32 = 4$

32 $\times 15 = 3$

33 $\times 9 = 6$

34 $\times 12 = 9$

35 $10 \times$ $= 8$

36 $12 \times$ $= 10$

37 $15 \times$ $= 10$

38 $20 \times$  $= 16$

Multiplying fractions

Copy and complete the multiplication tables.

1

×	9	15	8	12
$\frac{2}{3}$				
$\frac{1}{4}$				
$\frac{3}{5}$			$4\frac{4}{5}$	
$\frac{5}{6}$				

2

×	$\frac{1}{6}$	$\frac{3}{4}$	$\frac{4}{5}$	$\frac{7}{10}$
20				
16				
6				
30				

Predict the smallest and largest in each set. Calculate all three answers to check your predictions.

3. predict B C A

A $\frac{3}{5}$ × 1 0 = 6

3	A	$\frac{3}{5}$ × 10	B	12 × $\frac{2}{3}$	C	$\frac{5}{8}$ of 16
4	D	$\frac{4}{9}$ of 18	E	$\frac{6}{7}$ × 14	F	15 × $\frac{3}{4}$
5	G	12 × $\frac{5}{6}$	H	$\frac{3}{8}$ of 16	I	$\frac{4}{7}$ × 14
6	J	$\frac{3}{4}$ of 7	K	$\frac{2}{3}$ × 8	L	10 × $\frac{4}{5}$
7	M	$\frac{4}{5}$ × 11	N	10 × $\frac{3}{4}$	O	$\frac{1}{6}$ of 48

Explore

Choose a number, e.g. 8. Find two ways of making your number by multiplying a fraction and a whole number together.

$\frac{2}{3}$ × 12 = 8 $\frac{4}{5}$ × 10 = 8

Find two ways of making these numbers.

Numerators must be more than 1.

Choose some of your own numbers.

12   **20**

18

15   **24**

$\frac{3}{4}$ × 1 6 = 1 2

Fractions problems

1   David gets £12 a week for his paper round. He spends $\frac{1}{3}$ on magazines, $\frac{3}{4}$ of what is left on his bike and the rest on sweets. How much does he spend on sweets?

2   In Class 6, $\frac{1}{5}$ of the children go home for lunch. If 20 children stay in school for lunch, how many children go home?

3   In a bag of sweets $\frac{3}{8}$ are toffees, $\frac{1}{4}$ are soft centres and the rest are nut centres. If 20 sweets have soft centres, how many sweets are in the bag altogether?

4   In a school there are 210 pupils. 30 pupils catch a bus to school, 60 pupils cycle and the rest walk. What fraction of the pupils walk to school?

5   Josh has spent half his savings on a holiday, $\frac{1}{4}$ of what he had left over on clothes and $\frac{2}{3}$ of what was left after that on presents. He now has £15. How much did he start with?

6   Sally has 450 m left to run in a 3600 m race. What fraction of the race has she already run?

7   Children in a class of 30 are voting where to go on a school trip. $\frac{2}{5}$ want to go to a theme park, $\frac{4}{15}$ want to go to a football match and $\frac{1}{3}$ want to go on a boat trip. Which trip gets the most votes?

8   Carolyn starts school at 9 a.m. and finishes at 3 p.m. She has a break in the morning for $\frac{1}{4}$ hour. Lunchtime is $\frac{5}{6}$ hour. Afternoon break is $\frac{1}{3}$ hour. How long is Carolyn in lessons each day?

Dividing

Divide each number by 5, writing any remainder both as a fraction and as a decimal.

Do not use a calculator.

1 30   2 17   3 15   4 41   5 29

Repeat, dividing by these numbers in turn.

a 10   b 2   c 100   d 20   e 4

Write these divisions as decimals without using a calculator.

6 17 ÷ 2   7 193 ÷ 100   8 81 ÷ 10   9 151 ÷ 2

10 23 ÷ 4   11 41 ÷ 4   12 117 ÷ 20   13 $\frac{33}{5}$

14 $\frac{47}{4}$ 15 $\frac{63}{2}$ 16 $\frac{51}{10}$ 17 $\frac{73}{20}$

Write each fraction as a decimal, using a calculator if necessary.

18 $\frac{1}{8}$ $\frac{2}{8}$ $\frac{3}{8}$ $\frac{4}{8}$ $\frac{5}{8}$ $\frac{6}{8}$ $\frac{7}{8}$

Use your results to write these divisions as decimals.

19 46 ÷ 8   20 33 ÷ 8   21 $\frac{15}{8}$ 22 $\frac{70}{8}$

23 $\frac{55}{8}$ 24 17 ÷ 8   25 29 ÷ 8   26 $\frac{87}{8}$

A bus company takes groups of people on sightseeing tours. Calculate how many buses are needed for each group.

27 92 people   28 114 people   29 74 people
13-seater buses   12-seater buses   14-seater buses

30 168 people   31 136 people   32 87 people
15-seater buses   11-seater buses   9-seater buses

e How many 16-seater buses are needed for each group?

Dividing

Each bill is shared equally. Write how much each person owes.

1 £137
   6 people

2 £128
   9 people

3 £209
   8 people

4 £189
   11 people

5 £146
   7 people

6 £393
   12 people

e Round the amount each pays to the nearest pound.

Write how many days each person works.

7. $84 \div 8 = 10\frac{4}{8}$

   $10\frac{1}{2}$ days

7 84 hours
   8 hours/day

8 94 hours
   6 hours/day

9 102 hours
   9 hours/day

10 105 hours
    4 hours/day

11 66 hours
    7 hours/day

12 206 hours
    8 hours/day

Explore

Use one set of number cards, 0 to 9.

Investigate different ways of placing the cards to create links like these between fractions and decimals.

Dividing

1   John earns £23 a week stacking boxes in his dad's shop. If he saves all of his earnings, how many weeks does he need to work to pay for a £150 mountain bike?

2   Ruth has 320 stamps to sell. She puts them into packets of 12 to sell at £1·50 a pack. How many packs can she sell? How much will she earn if she sells all the packs?

3   Gary is moving bricks from the front of the house to the back. He can fit 7 bricks on his hod. If he has 85 bricks to move, how many trips must he make?

4   A charity walk from Alston to Bunston is 470 km long. The walk is organised as a relay, with each person walking 9 km. How many people are needed to complete the walk?

Problems

5   On an aeroplane each row of seats holds 9 passengers. How many complete rows will 230 passengers take up?

6   Stickers come in packets of 6. Sally needs 258 stickers to complete her album. If she has no repeats in the packs of stickers that she buys, what is the fewest number of packs she needs to buy to complete the album?

7   The school minibus holds 12 children. There are 237 children going to camp. How many trips will the minibus need to make?

8   Pinda is buying cans of cola for the school fête. He has £16 to spend. Cans cost 23p each. How many cans of cola can he buy?

Explore

Use a calculator.

   10 ÷ 3 = 3·3333333

In this division, 3 is a 1-digit recurring decimal.

   100 ÷ 11 = 9·090909

In this division, 09 is a 2-digit recurring decimal.

Investigate different divisions which give 1-digit and 2-digit recurring decimals.

Decimal numbers

Copy each number line. Draw pointers to show the position of each number. Write each set of numbers in order, smallest to largest.

1 3·2 3·45 3·6 3·65 3·7

3 ————————————————— 4

2 5·61 5·68 5·635 5·6 5·645

5·6 ————————————————— 5·7

Write each set of numbers in order, using '<'.

3. 3·24 < 3·25 < 3·26

3 3·24, 3·25, 3·26

4 6·92, 7·4, 7·16

5 4·27, 5·4, 4·5

6 4·85, 4·9, 4·09

7 24·351, 23·451, 23·54

8 5·1, 5·06, 5·61

9 3·24, 3·236, 3·62

10 6·477, 6·475, 6·48

Use the table to write the information about the cats in order from smallest to largest.

	Cat 1	Cat 2	Cat 3	Cat 4	Cat 5
Height (cm)	35·4	34·5	34·45	34·54	34·454
Weight (kg)	1·45	1·5	1·415	1·4	1·54
Tail length (cm)	28	29·1	28·45	28·6	28·591
Longest whisker (cm)	6·455	6·545	6·55	6·504	6·5

11 heights

12 weights

13 tail lengths

14 longest whisker lengths

 **Explore**

Use four digit cards and a decimal point card.

Investigate making different decimal numbers.

How many can you make between 1 and 5?

Write them in order.

Adding and subtracting decimals

Write the next five numbers in each sequence using these rules.

I. 3·8, 3·9, 4·0, 4·1,...

I   3·8 add 0·1

2   4·96 add 0·01

3   2·3 subtract 0·1

4   5·03 subtract 0·01

Copy and complete.

?

5	5·8 − 0·1	6	3 − 0·1	7	8·35 + 0·1
8	4·26 + 0·01	9	9·24 − 0·01	10	4·63 − 0·1
11	3·99 + 0·01	12	7·96 + 0·1	13	4·1 − 0·01
14	5·8 + 0·01	15	6 − 0·01	16	6·325 + 0·01
17	2·948 + 0·1	18	5·736 − 0·1	19	3·072 − 0·1

Write what must be added to the star numbers to make each number.

?

16·57   20 16·67   21 26·57   22 17   23 16·58   24 17·57

4·99   25 5·09   26 5   27 5·99   28 14·99   29 10

Write what must be subtracted from the star numbers to make each number.

3·22   30 2·22   31 3·12   32 3·21   33 3   34 2·92

5·04   35 4·04   36 5   37 4·94   38 5·03   39 4·1

Adding and subtracting decimals

Write how heavy each bag of flour is after 30 g of flour is added. ?

1. 1·85 kg
2. 2·34 kg
3. 3·7 kg
4. 2·98 kg

Write how much is left in each bottle after 70 ml is poured out. ?

5. 1·28 l
6. 1·34 l
7. 2·5 l
8. 2·435 l

Write how far each cyclist has travelled after they ride another 87 m. ?

9. 2·7 km
10. 3·41 km
11. 4·572 km
12. 5·64 km

Write how long each piece of wood is after 45 mm is cut off. ?

13. 2·565 m
14. 1·67 m
15. 2·42 m
16. 3·2 m

Adding decimals

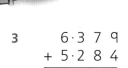
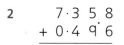

Copy and complete these additions. Estimate first.

```
1    5·7 2 3
   + 2·8 6 9
   ─────────
```

```
2    7·3 5 8
   + 0·4 9 6
   ─────────
```

```
3    6·3 7 9
   + 5·2 8 4
   ─────────
```

```
4    7·1 4 6
     2·3 9 7
   + 0·4 8 5
   ─────────
```

```
5    8·7 1 6
     9·4 8 5
   + 1·3 9 7
   ─────────
```

```
6    2·1 6 8
     4·3 7 9
   + 5·2 8 6
   ─────────
```

A	B	C	D	E	F

1·762 kg	3·546 kg	356 g	4·73 kg	2540 g	0·48 kg

Find the total weight of these boxes.

7 A and B

8 C and D

9 E and F

10 A, C and E

11 B, C and D

12 E, B, C and A

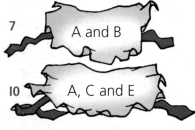
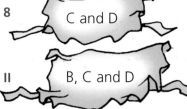
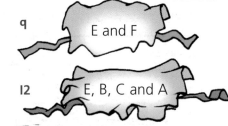

Write the total for each set of numbers.

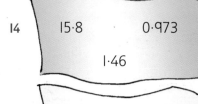

13   31·8
          2·746

14   15·8   0·973
           1·46

15   2·794   13·86
            143·7

16   0·058   15·9
      6·73   5·492

17   13   7·654
            2·8

18   9·3   7·582
      15·6   23   0·49

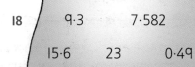
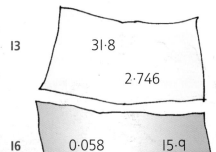
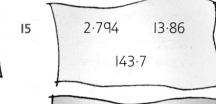

Adding decimals

Calculate how far each snail travels.

1. morning   afternoon
   1·324 m   0·763 m

2. morning   afternoon
   1·582 m   2·346 m

3. morning   afternoon
   186 cm   1·39 m

4. morning   afternoon
   46 cm   0·852 m
   evening
   1·7 m

5. morning   afternoon
   658 mm   1·27 m
   evening
   69 cm

6. morning   afternoon
   1·356 m   0·782 m
   evening
   552 mm

Problems

7. Danny drinks 2·356 l of water on Monday, 857 ml on Tuesday, 1·6 l on Wednesday and 2·78 l on Thursday. How much does he need to drink on Friday to make a total of 10 l?

8. Billie measures the exact distance to cycle from home to her friends' houses. It is 2·436 km to Helen's house, 1·728 km to Jamie's and 0·874 km to Gita's. She cycles to Helen's and back in the morning, to Jamie's and back in the afternoon, and to Gita's and back in the evening. How far has Billie cycled?

Explore

Use one set of digit cards, 1 to 9.

Make two decimal numbers between 1 and 10 using four cards each.

The digits in each number must be consecutive, e.g. 5·432 and 6·789.

Calculate the total of the two numbers.

How many different totals can you make which are more than 10?

Subtracting decimals

> Copy and complete these subtractions. Estimate first.

1.
```
   5·7 2 3
 - 1·4 6 8
 _____
```

2.
```
   6·9 4 7
 - 2·3 1 9
 _____
```

3.
```
   4·7 3 5
 - 2·5 9 6
 _____
```

4.
```
  2 1·6 4 7
 - 1 4·3 5 8
 _____
```

5.
```
  1 9·7 4 1
 -   8·3 9 4
 _____
```

6.
```
  1 1·5 2 6
 -   7·6 8 3
 _____
```

7.
```
   4·3 9 2
 - 0·1 6 8
 _____
```

8.
```
  1 2·7 0 4
 -   9·3 5 1
 _____
```

9.
```
   8·0 0 6
 - 1·2 7 8
 _____
```

> Calculate the difference between the distances cycled by each cyclist on two days.

10. Monday 13·275 km — Tuesday 25·763 km

11. Saturday 8·346 km — Sunday 11·751 km

12. Friday 16·348 km — Saturday 5·271 km

13. Wednesday 9·347 km — Thursday 12·562 km

14. Tuesday 24·385 km — Wednesday 9·471 km

15. Sunday 32·564 km — Monday 48·319 km

e Find the average (mean) number of kilometres cycled by each cyclist.

Subtracting decimals

Copy and complete these subtractions.

1
```
    6·4 2
 −  5·3 5 8
 ─────────
```

2
```
    7·1 6
 −  3·4 7 2
 ─────────
```

3
```
    5·0 4
 −  2·7 5 1
 ─────────
```

4
```
   1 1·8
 −   1·6 5 3
 ─────────
```

5
```
   1 4·3
 − 1 0·5 4 6
 ─────────
```

6
```
    9·7
 −  4·3 0 8
 ─────────
```

7
```
   1 5·0 4
 −   4·3 6 5
 ─────────
```

8
```
   1 0·0 3
 −   4·5 4 9
 ─────────
```

9
```
    8·0
 −  4·6 5 2
 ─────────
```

e Round the answers to 2 decimal places.

Calculate how much taller the trees have grown in the last year.

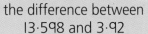

10 last year 5·63 m
now 6·725 m

11 last year 4·821 m
now 5·237 m

12 last year 7·436 m
now 9·2 m

13 last year 11.735 m
now 13.46 m

14 last year 1·524 m
now 1·8 m

15 last year 6·358 m
now 7·59 m

Complete these calculations.

16 2·275 less than 9·064

17 the difference between 13·598 and 3·92

18 20·223 subtract 12·534

Each of the answers is a 3-place decimal made from the digits 6, 7, 8 and 9.

Create three more subtractions which have 3-place decimal answers made from the same digits.

33

Decimal problems

> Choose an appropriate method to calculate the answers to these problems.

1 Ray is putting a fence along two sides of his garden. One side is 12·75 m long and the other side is 10·25 m long. How much fencing does he need?

2 Electric cable comes in reels 200 m long. Dave uses one length 15·4 m long and another length 22·73 m long. How much cable is left on the reel?

3 A cement mixer contains 80 l of cement. Bob pours some cement into a wheelbarrow. He uses 42·7 l to make a path and has 4·8 l left in the wheelbarrow. How much is left in the mixer?

4 A room is 3·56 m wide. The carpet that comes from the factory is 5 m wide. How much must be cut off the width of the carpet to make it fit in the room?

5 The side wall of a house will be 9·3 m high when it is finished. The builders have completed 4·68 m of the wall. How much more do they have to build?

6 A kitchen is 3·75 m long. There are three kitchen units to fit. One is 80 cm wide, one is 1·6 m wide and one is 95 cm wide. The refrigerator is 75 cm wide. Will they all fit along one wall? Explain your answer.

7 Kate uses 2·5 l of paint to paint the kitchen, 2·85 l to paint the dining room and 3·48 l to paint the living room. How much paint does she use altogether?

8 The builder is unloading 300 kg of sand. He drops a bag and 14·62 kg falls out. How much sand is left?

Powers and prime factors

Write these products using powers.

1. 3^2

I	3×3	2	$4 \times 4 \times 4$
3	$2 \times 2 \times 2 \times 2 \times 2$	4	5×5
5	$6 \times 6 \times 6 \times 6$	6	$10 \times 10 \times 10$
7	$1 \times 1 \times 1 \times 1$	8	$7 \times 7 \times 7 \times 7 \times 7 \times 7$
9	$2 \times 2 \times 2 \times 5 \times 5$	10	$3 \times 3 \times 7 \times 7 \times 7 \times 7$
11	$2 \times 2 \times 3 \times 3 \times 3 \times 11 \times 11$	12	$2 \times 3 \times 2 \times 3 \times 3$

Write the value of these.

?

13	4^2	14	2^3	15	7^2	16	2^4
17	10^3	18	2^6	19	3^3	20	2^5

Write these numbers as the product of prime factors.

21. $60 = 2^2 \times 3 \times 5$

21	60	22	33	23	18
24	42	25	56	26	144
27	500	28	120	29	2464

Explore

Create a table to show the first six powers of numbers.

Write the first six powers of 2, 3 and 4.

Extend to the powers of some other numbers.

Use a calculator to check them.

Investigate using a calculator to find powers.

Try pressing 3 × = = = ...

Powers

Write the number for each.

1   I am 2 less than 2 to the power of 3. Who am I?

2   I am 3 more than the second power of 2. Who am I?

3   I am the next power of 2 after 16. Who am I?

4   2 to the power of me is 64. Who am I?

5   3 to the power of me plus 5 is 14. Who am I?

6   2 to the power of me is 4 to the power of 2. Who am I?

7   Me to the power of 3 is 25 more than 10 to the power of 2. Who am I?

8   I am half of 10 cubed. Who am I?

9   Me to the power of 2 is 4 more than 2 to the power of 5. Who am I?

10   10 to the power of me is one million. Who am I?

Write these as powers of 10. The number of:

11   centimetres in a metre

12   grams in a kilogram

13   metres in a kilometre

14   millimetres in a metre

15   centimetres in a kilometre

16   centilitres in a litre

17   millimetres in a kilometre

18   millilitres in a litre

19   square millimetres in a square centimetre

20   square centimetres in a square metre

Explore

These are the powers of 2: 2, 4, 8, 16, 32, ...

Their units digits are: 2, 4, 8, 6, 2, ...

Extend the list of the powers of 2 to look for a pattern.

Investigate patterns in the units digits of powers of 3, then in the powers of other numbers.

Use your results to write the units digit of these numbers.

2^{10} 3^{12} 4^7 6^{11}

$^-$10   0   10

Write each child's bank statement.

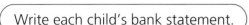

I. $^+$£8 add $^-$£5 = $^+$£4

1 deposits £8 withdraws £5	**2** deposits £9 withdraws £4	**3** deposits £3·50 withdraws £2	**4** deposits £1·80 withdraws £4·50
5 withdraws £13·60 deposits £5·50	**6** withdraws £1·25 deposits £7	**7** deposits £12 withdraws £5·80	**8** withdraws £4·75 withdraws £1·50
9 deposits £9 deposits £13 withdraws £18	**10** withdraws £17 deposits £16 deposits £15	**11** withdraws £3·50 deposits £10 withdraws £6·80	**12** deposits £25 withdraws £4·50 withdraws £11·75

Complete these additions.

13 $^+$3 add $^-$2	**14** $^+$5 add $^-$4	**15** $^-$3 add $^+$6
16 $^+$4 add $^+$3	**17** $^-$4 add $^-$5	**18** $^-$7 add $^+$12
19 ($^+$3) + ($^-$4)	**20** ($^+$5) + ($^-$6)	**21** ($^-$7) + ($^-$1)
22 ($^-$5) + ($^+$2)	**23** ($^+$3) + ($^+$4·5)	**24** ($^+$1·5) + ($^-$2·6)
25 ($^+$5) + ($^+$3) + ($^-$4)	**26** ($^-$4) + ($^-$3) + ($^-$7)	**27** ($^+$5) + ($^-$3) + ($^-$10)
28 ($^+$74) + ($^-$63) + ($^-$18)	**29** ($^-$48) + ($^+$17) + ($^+$53)	**30** ($^+$0·3) + ($^-$0·8) + ($^-$0·5)

Explore

Write different additions which have an answer of $^-$3, by:

- adding two negative numbers
- adding a positive and a negative number
- adding two positive numbers and one negative number
- adding two negative numbers and one positive number.

Travel up and down the lift to help you solve these.

1	$^+5$ subtract $^+2$	2	$^+2$ subtract $^+5$
3	$^+3$ subtract $^-1$	4	$^-2$ subtract $^+5$
5	$^-4$ subtract $^-7$	6	$^-3$ subtract $^-1$
7	$(^+8) - (^-3)$	8	$(^-6) + (^+4)$
9	$(^+1.5) - (^-2)$	10	$(^-3.5) - (^+1)$
11	$(^-3) - (^-1.5)$	12	$(^{+}\frac{1}{2}) - (^-2\frac{1}{4})$

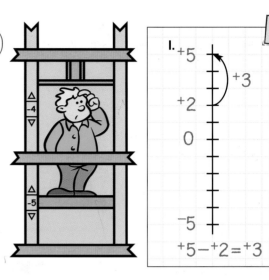

$^+5 - {^+2} = {^+3}$

Complete these input and output tables.

13	add $^-3$	in	$^+3$	$^-4$	$^-1$	0	$^+5$	$^-3$	$^+1.3$	$^-\frac{1}{2}$
		out								

14	subtract $^+5$	in	$^+1$	$^-2$	$^+6$	$^-7$	0	$^-5$	$^+1.8$	$^-\frac{3}{4}$
		out								

15	subtract $^-3$	in	$^-4$	$^+2$	$^-1$	$^+7$	$^+1.5$	$^-2.5$	0	$^{+}\frac{1}{2}$
		out								

In an addition pyramid, each number is the total of the two numbers directly below.

In a subtraction pyramid, each number is the result of subtracting the second number from the first of the two numbers below.

Complete these pyramids for both addition and subtraction.

Invent some of your own.

16

$^+3$	$^-2$	$^-4$	$^+5$	$^-1$

17

$^+6$	$^-3$	$^+5$	$^-7$	$^+1$

Multiplying decimals

Check the grid to see if it shows the correct answer for 25·7 × 7·3.

	20	5	0·7	
7	140	35	4·9	179·9
0·3	6	1·5	0·21	7·71
	146	36·5	5·11	**187·61**

Use the grid method to find these products. Estimate first.

1	4·32 × 5·7	2	36·4 × 4·8	3	19·7 × 3·6
4	26·5 × 1·9	5	58·7 × 9·3	6	61·2 × 4·3

The caretaker is going to paint the school's ceilings. He wants to know the area of each ceiling to work out how much paint he needs.

Use long multiplication to find the area of each ceiling. Estimate first.

7	Y1/Y2 corridor 35·6 m × 4·3 m	8	Y3/Y4 corridor 28·7 m × 3·9 m	9	Y5/Y6 corridor 23·6 m × 4·6 m
10	staffroom corridor 13·4 m × 2·9 m	11	school entrance 15·6 m × 7·3 m	12	library 12·8 m × 6·4 m

 Each tin of paint covers 15 m². How many tins does the caretaker need in total?

The children are making banners for the school fête. Each child cuts a strip of paper. Predict which piece in each pair has the greater area. Calculate the area of each strip of paper and the difference in area between them.

13	John	25·7 cm by 4·6 cm	14	Tim	31·6 cm by 3·9 cm
	Karen	31·2 cm by 3·4 cm		Sumoyee	42·7 cm by 2·8 cm
15	Lois	43·8 cm by 2·7 cm	16	Sara	28·6 cm by 4·9 cm
	Dharmendra	31·7 cm by 3·5 cm		Tiffany	26·7 cm by 5·3 cm

REED PRIMARY SCHOOL

Multiplying decimals

Use long multiplication to find the total cost of each of these coach tours. Estimate first.

TOMMY'S COACH TRIPS

1. Dinosaur World
   £2·75
   28 people

2. Scary Towers
   £4·45
   53 people

3. Walter's Kingdom
   £3·55
   24 people

4. Water Crash
   £4·85
   32 people

5. Safari Woods
   £5·35
   18 people

6. Rollercoaster Valley
   £6·65
   44 people

At Dinosaur World there is a footstep trail to follow. Each dinosaur has a long footstep. Calculate how long each dinosaur trail is.

7. footstep 4·35 m
   28 steps

8. footstep 3·72 m
   32 steps

9. footstep 5·46 m
   41 steps

10. footstep 2·86 m
    63 steps

11. footstep 4·19 m
    45 steps

12. footstep 5·08 m
    53 steps

ℯ Estimate each answer in feet.

Explore

Use the number cards shown to make a 2-place decimal number and a 2-digit number, e.g. 4·37 and 56.

4 · 3 7   5 6

Multiply them together.

How many different answers can you make between 200 and 250?

40 Write the multiplications and list the answers in order.

Dividing decimals

Calculate how many hours per week each person has worked at the supermarket.

```
        3 1 · 6
  8)2 5 2 · 8
1.  2 4 0 · 0    8 x 30
      1 2 · 8
        8 · 0    8 x 1
        4 · 8
        4 · 8    8 x 0·6
          0
```

1 Jeevan
252·8 hours
8 weeks

2 Kate
200·2 hours
7 weeks

3 Danny
147·6 hours
9 weeks

4 Ray
142·2 hours
6 weeks

5 Peta
213·5 hours
5 weeks

6 Sam
268·8 hours
7 weeks

7 Ben
106·4 hours
4 weeks

8 Maya
149·6 hours
8 weeks

SPECIAL OFFER

Check each answer by multiplying.

Each group shares the café bill equally. Write how much each person pays.

9 £85·44
16 people

10 £80·64
12 people

11 £84·78
18 people

12 £84·89
13 people

13 £78·54
21 people

14 £92·14
17 people

e How much do they each pay if they leave a 10% tip?

Estimate, then copy and complete each division.

15 $98·4 \div 8 =$

16 $88·2 \div 6 =$

17 $90·3 \div 7 =$

18 $77·04 \div 12 =$

Check each answer by multiplying.

19 $75·53 \div 13 =$

20 $28·64 \div 16 =$

Dividing decimals

Change each division into an equivalent division using whole numbers only.

1. $426 \div 2 \cdot 7 = 4260 \div 27$

$$
\begin{array}{r}
157\frac{7}{9} \\
27)\overline{4260} \\
2700 \qquad 27 \times 100 \\
\overline{1560} \\
1350 \qquad 27 \times 50 \\
\overline{210} \\
189 \qquad 27 \times 7 \\
\overline{21} \qquad \frac{21}{27} = \frac{7}{9}
\end{array}
$$

1	$426 \div 2 \cdot 7$	**2**	$38 \cdot 6 \div 1 \cdot 7$
3	$625 \div 0 \cdot 6$	**4**	$5430 \div 6 \cdot 8$
5	$21 \cdot 3 \div 0 \cdot 42$	**6**	$4 \cdot 76 \div 2 \cdot 4$

The food factory packs vegetables in boxes to send to the supermarket. Write how many boxes are needed to pack each type of vegetable.

Calculate the weight of vegetables needed to fill the last box for each. Write the answers correct to 1 decimal place.

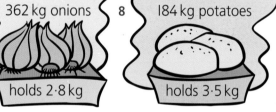

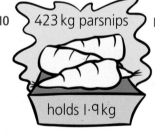

7 362 kg onions — holds 2·8 kg

8 184 kg potatoes — holds 3·5 kg

9 237 kg carrots — holds 4·6 kg

10 423 kg parsnips — holds 1·9 kg

11 516 kg turnips — holds 2·6 kg

12 258 kg cabbages — holds 3·2 kg

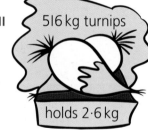

Divide each star number by each circle number. Write the answers correct to 1 decimal place.

452

187

326

1·6

2·7

3·4

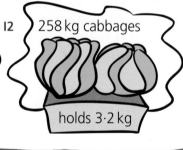

Decimal problems

> Choose an appropriate method to calculate the answers to these problems.

1 Lemonade comes in 1·5 l bottles. How many 0·3 ml glasses can be filled from 3 bottles?

2 Riley makes 12 cakes using 0·35 kg of flour. How much flour would he need to make 48 cakes?

3 Ham is sold in 250 g packs. Each pack contains 5 slices of ham. How many slices would there be in a family-size pack which weighs 1·5 kg?

4 At a party 16 children each receive a bag containing 0·018 kg of chocolate. If the children eat all of their chocolate, how much chocolate is eaten altogether?

5 Carly is organizing an apple-bobbing game. One kilogram of apples costs £1·32 and each apple weighs 0·125 kg. How many apples can she buy for £3·96?

6 Marlon makes jelly by adding 0·375 l of boiling water and 0·15 l of cold water to jelly cubes. To make a very large jelly he uses 0·6 l of cold water. How much boiling water does he need?

7 At a party the children drink 12 bottles which each contain 0·375 l of cola, 3 bottles each containing 1·5 l of lemonade and 7 bottles of cherryade each containing 750 ml. How much liquid is drunk altogether?

8 A slice of bread weighs 0·017 kg. Chris uses 36 slices of bread to make sandwiches for a party. What is the total weight of the bread he uses?

43

Calculating percentages

Calculate these percentages, without using a calculator. Find the percentages shown in the hint bubbles to help you.

1   11% of 3500 m   (find 10% and 1%)

2   53% of 1600 km   (find 50% and 1%)

3   14% of 4300 km   (find 10%, 5% and 1%)

4   44% of 2800 m   (find 50%, 5% and 1%)

5   89% of 3700 km   (find 100%, 10% and 1%)

6   119% of 8400 m   (find 100%, 20% and 1%)

Choose your own method to find these percentages without using a calculator.

7   21% of £600

8   26% of £1400

9   52% of £1100

10 48% of £6·50

Check each calculation using the percentage key on your calculator.

11 18% of £25 000

12 121% of £800

Calculate, without using a calculator, the total number of votes received by each party in each election.

13 **Wetchurch Election**

Pink Party	Yellow Party	Purple Party
31%	43%	26%

Total Votes: 15 000

14 **Coldham Election**

Pink Party	Yellow Party	Purple Party
72%	9%	19%

Total Votes: 18 000

Election Day

15 **Dryfield Election**

Pink Party	Yellow Party	Purple Party
18%	63%	19%

Total Votes: 24 000

16 **Hotpatch Election**

Pink Party	Yellow Party	Purple Party
46%	22%	32%

Total Votes: 32 000

e Calculate the total votes for each party in all four elections.

Calculating percentages

Calculate these percentages, using a calculator, by:

changing the percentage to a decimal and multiplying

changing the percentage to a fraction and multiplying

| ? |

1 26% of £4300

2 18% of £700

3 29% of £1800

writing 1%, then multiplying

using the percentage key

4 43% of £4700

5 17% of £3600

6 89% of £800

Calculate how much each price is reduced by, then write the new price of each item.

| ? |

SKI SHACK

7 £87·50 50% off

8 £28 15% off

9 £19 35% off

10 £34·50 12% off

11 £76·20 $\frac{1}{3}$ off

12 £48 45% off

SNOW DEVIL

Solve each problem. Use a calculator to check your answers.

| ? |

13 A new car costs £14 000. The car dealer decides to reduce the price by 12%. How much is the new price?

14 The population of Wixham-on-Sea was 18 000 in 1990. It has increased by 12%. How many people live there now?

WIXHAM - ON - SEA POPULATION

Problems

15 A season ticket to watch the Rovers was £400 last year. Since gaining promotion next year's prices have increased by 16%. How much is a season ticket for next year?

ROVERS

16 Alex has joined a diet group because he is overweight. He weighs 98 kg and is trying to reduce his weight by 18%. What is his target weight?

17 CDs at the Music Store cost £13. In the sale they are reduced by 23%. How many CDs can Katie buy in the sale with £50, and how much change will she get?

18 Tim's bill for a meal at a restaurant is £55. He leaves 15% as a tip. What is his change from £100?

Calculating percentages

A shop displays its prices excluding VAT (value added tax). If VAT is 17·5%, write the total cost of each item.

I.
$$10\% \text{ of } £300 = £30$$
$$5\% \text{ of } £300 = £15$$
$$2\tfrac{1}{2}\% \text{ of } £300 = £7·50$$
$$VAT = £52·50$$
$$\text{Total cost} = £352·50$$

1 £300

2 £500

3 £900

4 £250

5 £840

6 £190

7 £398

8 £688

9 £424

e If £1 is ¥200 (Japanese yen), write how much each item would cost in Japan where consumer tax of 5% is added to each price.

Explore

A car costs £3000. It is worth 25% less than a year ago. How much did it cost a year ago? Use a calculator to help you.

Use your method to find how much these cars cost a year ago:

a £8100

b £2400

c £1200

d £990

cost now = £3000
cost 1 year ago = £x
£3000 is 25% less than £x

Fractions and percentages

Write these fractions as percentages.

1    $\frac{7}{10}$

2   $\frac{1}{4}$

3    $1\frac{3}{4}$

4    $2\frac{1}{2}$

5   $\frac{13}{100}$

6   $\frac{3}{8}$

Write these percentages as fractions.

7   75%   8   60%   9   150%   10   225%   11   87%   12   12·5%

Write these fractions as percentages by converting them into hundredths.

13. $\frac{3}{5} = \frac{60}{100} = 60\%$

13   $\frac{3}{5} = \frac{}{100}$

14   $\frac{7}{20} = \frac{}{100}$

15   $\frac{13}{50} = \frac{}{100}$

16   $\frac{27}{50} = \frac{}{100}$

17   $\frac{17}{25} = \frac{}{100}$

18   $\frac{34}{25} = \frac{}{100}$

Estimate the order of each set, from smallest to largest, by writing the letters in sequence.

Convert each fraction to a percentage, then write the correct order. Compare with your estimate.

19

A	B	C	D	E
$\frac{3}{5}$	$\frac{4}{10}$	$\frac{11}{20}$	$\frac{1}{2}$	$\frac{3}{4}$

20

F	G	H	I	J
$\frac{17}{25}$	$\frac{35}{100}$	$\frac{1}{4}$	$\frac{3}{2}$	$\frac{7}{10}$

21

K	L	M	N	O
$\frac{68}{200}$	$\frac{7}{10}$	$\frac{37}{50}$	$\frac{13}{20}$	$\frac{3}{5}$

22

P	Q	R	S	T
$\frac{6}{25}$	$\frac{5}{2}$	$\frac{3}{10}$	$\frac{7}{20}$	$\frac{69}{300}$

Write these percentages as fractions in their simplest form.

23	10%	24	25%	25	60%	26	5%
27	65%	28	80%	29	4%	30	120%
31	135%	32	72%	33	86%	34	64%
35	35%	36	18%	37	7%	38	12·5%

Fractions, decimals and percentages

Use your calculator to convert these fractions to percentages, correct to 1 decimal place.

1 $\dfrac{5}{6}$ 2 $\dfrac{4}{7}$ 3 $\dfrac{7}{9}$ 4 $\dfrac{3}{11}$ 5 $\dfrac{4}{3}$

6 $\dfrac{8}{15}$ 7 $\dfrac{5}{12}$ 8 $\dfrac{7}{8}$ 9 $\dfrac{11}{18}$ 10 $\dfrac{6}{13}$

For each set of cards, calculate the percentages shown.

| 3♥ | 4♠ | 2♦ | 5♣ |
| 4♠ | 5♥ | 9♥ | 5♦ |

11 black   12 red   13 spades   14 diamonds

15 clubs   16 more   17 odd   18 not
                    than 4   hearts

19 red   20 diamonds   21 clubs

22 black   23 hearts   24 even

| 5♦ | 3♣ | 5♥ | 2♦ | 7♥ | 8♠ |
| 4♣ | 9♦ | 9♣ | 10♦ | 6♥ | 6♠ |

25 black   26 red   27 hearts

28 clubs   29 more than 5   30 less than 5

Write '<', '>' or '=' between each pair.

31 $\dfrac{3}{4}$ ☐ 0·72   32 0·81 ♥ $\dfrac{4}{5}$ 33 $\dfrac{7}{20}$ ☐ 34%

34 45% ♦ $\dfrac{11}{25}$ 35 $\dfrac{3}{7}$ ☐ 43%   36 45% ♠ $\dfrac{5}{12}$

37 $\dfrac{5}{6}$ ☐ 0·8   38 $\dfrac{7}{8}$ ♣ 0·82   39 $\dfrac{4}{7}$ ☐ $\dfrac{6}{9}$

40 In a test $\dfrac{3}{7}$ of the children passed. What percentage failed?

41 In the Year 6 class 72% of children have had measles. What fraction have not?

Problems

42 When asked about their favourite season, $\dfrac{5}{12}$ voted for summer, $\dfrac{2}{7}$ voted for spring and $\dfrac{2}{9}$ for autumn. What percentage voted for winter?

43 At a match 40% of the fans are children and the rest are adults. If $\dfrac{4}{5}$ of the adults are male, what percentage of the fans are women?

Proportion

Write these ratios and proportions.

Crumble topping
(serves 6)
225 g flour
150 g brown sugar
75 g butter

Oat crunchies
(makes 12)
50 g whole oats
75 g porridge oats
100 g margarine
75 g brown sugar

Baked apple pudding
(serves 4)
450 g apples
50 g brown sugar
100 g butter
100 g caster sugar

Proportion of total weight which is:

1   butter
2   brown sugar
3   flour

8   whole oats
9   porridge oats
10 margarine
11 brown sugar

16 apples
17 butter
18 caster sugar
19 brown sugar

Ratio of:

4   butter to sugar
5   flour to butter
6   sugar to flour
7   butter to flour

12 sugar to margarine
13 whole oats to porridge oats
14 porridge oats to margarine
15 sugar to porridge oats

20 butter to apples
21 brown sugar to caster sugar
22 caster sugar to apples
23 apples to brown sugar

Write how much you will need to make these recipes:

24   butter for crumble topping to serve 12

25   brown sugar to make 8 oat crunchies

26   butter to make baked apple pudding for 6

Split these amounts in the given ratios.

27   500 g in the ratio of 2:3
28   400 g in the ratio of 3:5

29   640 g in the ratio of 7:9
30   480 g in the ratio of 2:3:7

31   1200 g in the ratio of 1:4:7
32   3·2 kg in the ratio of 3:5:8

Ratio

> Simplify these ratios, where possible, using whole numbers only.

I	8:12	2	4:6	3	12:6	4	5:6
5	7:21	6	28:21	7	12:9	8	8:6
9	15:21	10	14:35	II	18:24	12	35:45
13	6:18:36	14	9:45:72	15	15:25:65	16	8:20:44

> Write these ratios, using decimals, in the form **I** :

17. I : I·5

17	2:3	18	5:8	19	10:14	20	4:7
21	8:12	22	9:30	23	8:10	24	4:21
25	8:60	26	4:58	27	8:19	28	5:27

Problems

29 There are 25 teachers in a school of 450 children. Write the pupil to teacher ratio in its simplest form.

30 A cake is divided so that Janice gets 3 times as much as Jason. What proportion does Jason get?

31 In a class of 27, the boys to girls ratio is 4:5. How many girls are there?

32 Jo spends her day playing, eating and sleeping in the ratio 3:1:4. For how many hours does she play?

33 Richard, Karen and Lizzy have been given a total of £60 to divide in the ratio 2:3:5. How much does each get?

34 Concrete is made by mixing cement, sand and gravel in the ratio of 1:2:3. What proportion of the mix is a) sand, b) cement, c) gravel? If 18 m^3 of concrete is mixed, how much of each ingredient is needed?

Checking calculations

Round the two numbers in each calculation to approximate the answer.

Choose the nearest answer a, b or c. Use a calculator to check the correct answer.

			a	b	c	
D	1	$39\cdot4 + 27\cdot63 =$	$78\cdot13$	$67\cdot03$	$52\cdot43$	DELAYED
E	2	$568\cdot7 - 89\cdot5 =$	$348\cdot2$	$623\cdot2$	$479\cdot2$	
P						
A	3	$29\cdot7 \times 32 =$	$950\cdot4$	$601\cdot7$	$1032\cdot4$	ON TIME
R	4	$620\cdot62 \div 21\cdot7 =$	$47\cdot2$	$28\cdot6$	$301\cdot4$	
T						DELAYED
U	5	$279\cdot3 + 85\cdot41 =$	$1005\cdot44$	$424\cdot71$	$364\cdot71$	
R	6	18% of $841 =$	$151\cdot38$	$84\cdot2$	1624	LOST
E						
S	7	$536 \times 28 =$	1508	158	15008	**?**
	8	$479\cdot56 \div 38 =$	1262	$126\cdot2$	$12\cdot62$	

Write an inverse calculation for each of these and find the answer using a calculator. Are the answers given here correct?

9 $156\cdot2 + 73\cdot86 = 230\cdot06$

10 $26\cdot84 - 9\cdot735 = 17\cdot105$

11 $42\cdot17 + 0\cdot96 = 43\cdot13$

12 $5\cdot83 - 2\cdot714 = 3\cdot116$

13 $234\cdot8 \times 27 = 6339\cdot6$

14 $4\cdot78 \times 0\cdot65 = 3\cdot107$

15 $111\cdot39 \div 4\cdot74 = 23\cdot5$

16 $1054 \div 68 = 15\cdot5$

Checking calculations

> Write the last digit of the answer to each calculation.

1 39 718 − 2569

2 45 629 − 3724

3 58 × 762

4 35·23 + 17·6

5 28·72 − 14·6

6 27·54 + 2·66

7 5·29 − 4·753

8 7·9 × 8·3

9 28·6 × 7·3

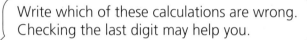

> Write which of these calculations are wrong.
> Checking the last digit may help you.

10 1562 − 398 = 1164

11 274·6 + 5·83 = 280·43

12 47·2 − 29·3 = 17·1

13 82 × 76 = 66 232

14 3·7 × 1·4 = 5·12

15 5·62 × 28 = 157·36

> Check whether each statement is correct. Write two
> alternative methods to calculate each answer.

16 Timmy the cat eats a whole tin of cat food every day for 3 weeks. Each tin costs 65p. Timmy's owner works out that it cost her £13·65.

17 A school sends out 476 letters to parents. The postage is 19p for each. The secretary has to pay a bill of £90·44 for stamps.

18 After a match two teams of 11 players are given a pie and pea supper which costs 78p per player. The total bill for the club is £17·16.

19 **Problems**

There are 4700 people at a concert. The organiser works out that there are 1222 children who pay half price. The children make up 26% of the audience.

20 Alice measures the surface of her homework desk as 99 cm long and 43 cm wide. She calculates that the area of her desk is 4257 cm^2.

21 The bookshop has 32 dictionaries on its shelf. The width of each is 4·7 cm. The owner calculates that the dictionaries use 1·504 m of shelf space.

Square numbers and cube numbers

> Write the value of these without using a calculator.

1 9^2	2 14^2	3 21^2	4 35^2
5 20^2	6 50^2	7 40^2	8 80^2
9 300^2	10 $(0.2)^2$	11 $(1.2)^2$	12 4^3
13 1^3	14 10^3	15 20^3	16 $(0.2)^3$
17 $(0.5)^2$	18 $(0.4)^3$	19 $(0.7)^2$	20 $(1.3)^2$

> Write an estimate for these squares. Use a calculator to write the exact answer. Check how close your estimate was.

21 28^2	22 17^2	23 21^2	24 32^2
25 $(4.8)^2$	26 $(7.2)^2$	27 $(9.1)^2$	28 $(1.9)^2$
29 $(6.3)^2$	30 $(10.5)^2$	31 $(9.9)^2$	32 $(12.7)^2$

Explore

Check that these squares are correct.

$15^2 = 225$
$25^2 = 625$
$35^2 = 1225$
$45^2 = 2025$

Try to spot a pattern, and use it to write these squares.

65^2 95^2 55^2 85^2

Write a description of the pattern.

Square roots and cube roots

Write the value of these roots without using a calculator.

1 $\sqrt{81}$

2 $\sqrt{1}$

3 $\sqrt{36}$

4 $\sqrt{49}$

5 $\sqrt{400}$

6 $\sqrt{144}$

7 $\sqrt{2500}$

8 $\sqrt{1600}$

9 $\sqrt{900}$

10 $\sqrt{6400}$

11 $\sqrt{40\,000}$

12 $\sqrt[3]{8}$

13 $\sqrt[3]{1000}$

14 $\sqrt[3]{1}$

15 $\sqrt[3]{125}$

16 $\sqrt[3]{64}$

17 $\sqrt{62\,500}$

18 $\sqrt[3]{216}$

19 $\sqrt{14\,400}$

20 $\sqrt[3]{8000}$

Write an estimate for these square roots.

Use a calculator to write the exact answer. Check how close your estimate was.

21 $\sqrt{150}$

22 $\sqrt{31}$

23 $\sqrt{96}$

24 $\sqrt{8}$

25 $\sqrt{300}$

26 $\sqrt{240}$

27 $\sqrt{1000}$

28 $\sqrt{3900}$

29 $\sqrt{15\,000}$

30 $\sqrt{8000}$

31 $\sqrt{630}$

32 $\sqrt{299}$

Explore

$13^2 = 169$ and $31^2 = 961$.

The reverse squares, 13 and 31 have reverse answers.

$102^2 = 10\,404$ and $201^2 = 40\,401$ are another pair of reverse squares.

Investigate other pairs of reverse squares.

Squares, cubes and roots

1 I am 4 less than the square root of 25. Who am I?

2 My square and my cube are identical. Who am I?

3 I am both a square number and a cubic number. Who am I?

4 My cube root is one quarter of me. Who am I?

5 Double my square to reach my cube. Who am I?

6 I am a 2-digit square number. My digits total 9 and have a difference of 3. Who am I?

7 I am a 2-digit cube number and both my digits are even. Who am I?

8 My cube root is the square of root 9. Who am I?

9 My square root is the cube root of 125. Who am I?

10 We are two 1-digit numbers. Our squares differ by 32. Who are we?

11 If you square me, add 1, then halve, I become 5 squared. Who am I?

12 When I am cubed I am 10 times more than when I am squared. Who am I?

13 I am a cubic number between 600 and 1000. Who am I?

14 I am the square root of a number which is 1 less than half of 10 squared. Who am I?

15 I am a digit which does not appear in any of the squares of the numbers from 1 to 20. Who am I?

Explore

Look at these additions.

The answers, 5, 45 and 17 are each the total of two square numbers.

$$1 + 4 = 5$$
$$9 + 36 = 45$$
$$1 + 16 = 17$$

Investigate other numbers, up to 50, which are the total of two square numbers.

square numbers

1, 4, 9, 16, ...

1 + 4 = 5

Using brackets

> Copy and complete these calculations.

1 $12 \times 2 + 4 =$

2 $43 + 40 \div 5 =$

3 $6 \times 8 + 46 =$

4 $140 \div 7 + 351 =$

5 $287 + 42 \times 6 =$

6 $29 + 126 \div 6 =$

7 $4 \times 3 + 5 \times 4 =$

8 $6 \times 2 + 5 \times 3 =$

9 $10 \div 5 - 6 \div 3 =$

10 $60 \div 5 + 8 \times 3 =$

11 $120 \div 10 - 24 \div 8 =$

12 $40 - 60 \div 4 + 7 =$

13 $70 + 5 \times 11 - 12 =$

14 $15 + 9 \times 8 - 7 =$

15 $2150 \div 5 + 5416 \div 8 =$

> Write true or false for each.

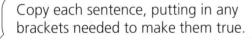

16 $(6 \times 5) \times 3 = 6 \times (5 \times 3)$

17 $(8 - 2) \times 3 = 8 - (2 \times 3)$

18 $(6 + 5) + 3 = 6 + (5 + 3)$

19 $(15 - 6) - 3 = 15 - (6 - 3)$

20 $(60 \div 6) \div 2 = 60 \div (6 \div 2)$

21 $(4 + 8) \times 2 = 4 + (8 \times 2)$

22 $(14 - 5) \times 2 = 14 - (5 \times 2)$

23 $(12 - 9) \div 3 = 12 - (9 \div 3)$

24 $(12 \div 3) \times 2 = 12 \div (3 \times 2)$

25 $(5 \times 6) \div 3 = 5 \times (6 \div 3)$

> Copy each sentence, putting in any brackets needed to make them true.

26 $4 \times 3 + 6 = 36$

27 $4 \times 2 + 7 = 15$

28 $6 \times 8 - 2 = 36$

29 $7 \times 3 - 4 = 17$

30 $40 \div 4 \times 5 = 50$

31 $40 \div 4 \times 5 = 2$

32 $20 \div 4 + 1 = 4$

33 $20 \div 4 + 1 = 6$

34 $8 + 12 \div 3 + 4 = 16$

35 $42 - 5 \times 3 - 16 = 11$

Calculations with brackets

> Copy and complete these.

1. $(26 + 7) \times 4 =$

2. $5 \times (18 - 7) =$

3. $(15 + 9) \times 7 =$

4. $(42 \times 10) \div 20 =$

5. $(75 \times 4) \div 3 =$

6. $(165 \div 3) \times 2 =$

7. $48 - (27 + 3) \div 3 =$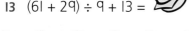

8. $15 + 8 \times (22 - 19) =$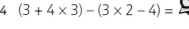

9. $(16 - 7) \times 7 + 17 =$

10. $17 + (27 + 6) \div 3 =$

11. $(16 - 9) \times 4 - 25 =$

12. $100 - 8 \times (6 + 4) =$

13. $(61 + 29) \div 9 + 13 =$

14. $(3 + 4 \times 3) - (3 \times 2 - 4) =$

15. $(17 - 6 \times 2) + (2 \times 2 + 3) =$

> Copy and complete.

16. $2 \times (5 + 3)^2$

17. $18 - (16 - 14)^2$

18. $(7 - 5)^3 + 4$

19. $4^2 + (7 - 6)^4$

20. $3^3 - (3 + 2)^2$

21. $(2^2 + 3^2)^2$

22. $(7^2 - 6^2)^2$

23. $\dfrac{4^3}{(3 + 5)^2}$

24. $\dfrac{4^2 - 1}{2^3 - 3}$

Explore

Use the digits 1, 2, 3, 4, 5 only.

Create calculations using all five digits once each.

Each calculation must include a bracket and a power.

Can you find different ways to make these numbers?

44   59   29

How many numbers up to 20 can you make?

$(4 + 3)^2 - (1 \times 5) = 44$

$(1 + 3 + 4)^2 - 5 = 59$

$2^3 + (5 \times 4) + 1 = 29$

Using letters

Write the lengths of these sticks of rock.

1. $a + l$

1 $\boxed{a \quad | \quad l}$

2 $\boxed{x \quad | \quad x}$

Remember to use letters like this:

$$3 \times y \to 3y$$
$$a \times b \to ab \text{ or } ba$$
$$d \div 5 \to \frac{d}{5}$$
$$p \times p \to p^2$$

3 $\boxed{p \quad | \quad p \quad | \quad p}$

4 $\boxed{q \quad | \quad q \quad | \quad 3}$

5 $\boxed{1 \quad | \quad y \quad | \quad 2}$

6 $\boxed{z \mid z \mid 2 \mid z \mid z}$

Write the perimeters of these doughnuts.

?

7 p / p

8 b b / b

9 n n / n n

10 w w / w w / w

11 p / q

12 a / b / c

13 3 / t

14 y / x

15 g / f / f

Write the areas of these postcards.

?

16 x / x

17 5 / 5

18 a / b

19 q / 3

20 a / l / 4

21 $p + l$ / $p + l$

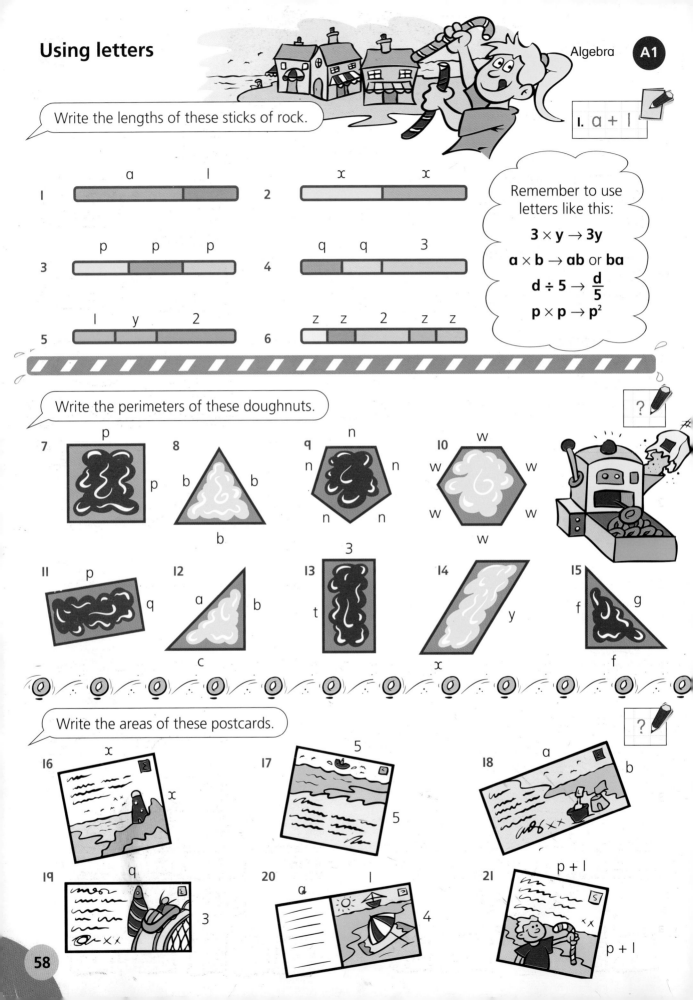

Using letters

Write these using symbols.

1. 6 add z
2. 4 take away p

1. $6 + z$

3. double q
4. y add 8
5. c subtract q
6. the total of f and g
7. 3 less than t
8. z add 5 subtract y

9. 5 times a
10. b times 3
11. g multiplied by 4
12. 6 multiplied by p
13. 5 divided by x
14. y divided by 4

15. half of j
16. p divided by q
17. double h
18. treble w
19. z multiplied by itself
20. d squared

Write the final expressions.

21. $x + 3 - p$

21. x, add 3, then take away p
22. y, subtract 6, then add z
23. a, double it, then add 3
24. m, treble it, then take away 5

25. p, multiply it by 10, then add q
26. d, add 5, then add d
27. c, halve it, then add 4
28. 4, add z, then double the total

29. t, subtract 5, then treble the total
30. z, double it, add 4, then take away 1
31. h, multiply it by itself, then add 10
32. q, square it, then subtract 3

Write what comes out of each machine.

33

in → ×3 → out

34

in → ×3 → +2 → out

a. a
b. 2
c. x + 1
d. a + b
e. 2a

a. 4
b. ½
c. f
d. c + 1
e. 2 + q

Problems

1. A tree was t cm tall last year. Since then it has grown another 12 cm. How tall is it now?

2. There are x people in the room, and 3 walk out. How many people are left in the room?

3. Anna is 4 years younger than her sister Debbie. Debbie is h years old. How old is Anna?

4. Jars of marmalade weigh g kilograms each. How much do 6 jars weigh?

5. There are x biscuits in a tin. They are shared equally among 5 children. How many biscuits does each child get?

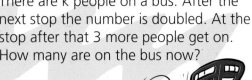

6. Jed had saved £p, and then won £q in a competition. He spent £4 on a book about animals. How much has he now?

7. There are k people on a bus. After the next stop the number is doubled. At the stop after that 3 more people get on. How many are on the bus now?

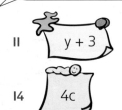

8. The perimeter of an equilateral triangle is n cm. What is the length of one of its sides?

9. The length of a rectangle is 4 cm more than its width, which is z cm. What are the perimeter and area of the rectangle?

10. A square has a side of length g cm. A larger square has a side of length f cm. What is the difference in their areas?

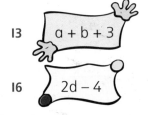

Invent your own problems to match each of these answers.

11. $y + 3$

12. $z - 2$

13. $a + b + 3$

14. $4c$

15. $\dfrac{p}{3}$

16. $2d - 4$

Using letters

Write the blue dates.

M	T	W	T	F	S	S
						1
2	3	4	5	6	7	8
9	10	11	12	13	14	15
16	17	18	19	20	21	22
23	24	25	26	27	28	29
30	31					

1 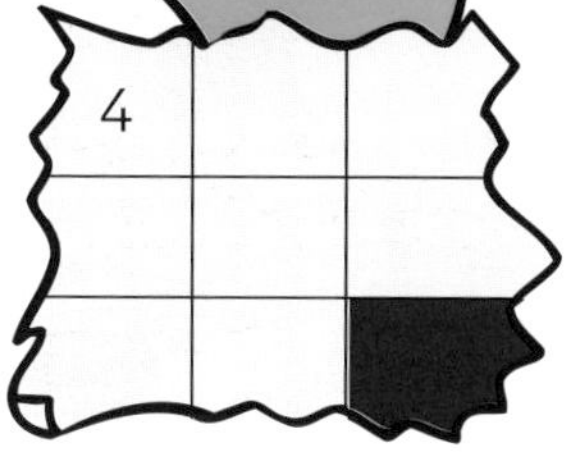 4

2  19

3 28

Write the red dates in terms of x.

4 x

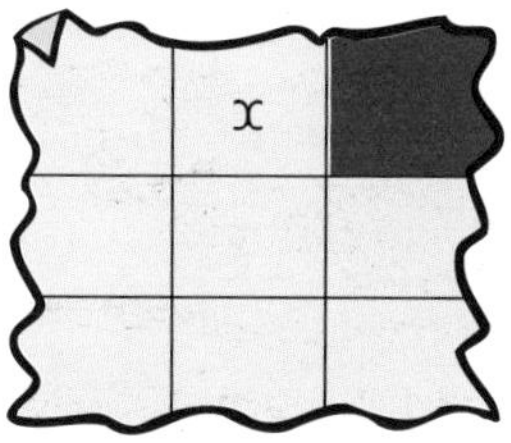

5 x

6 x

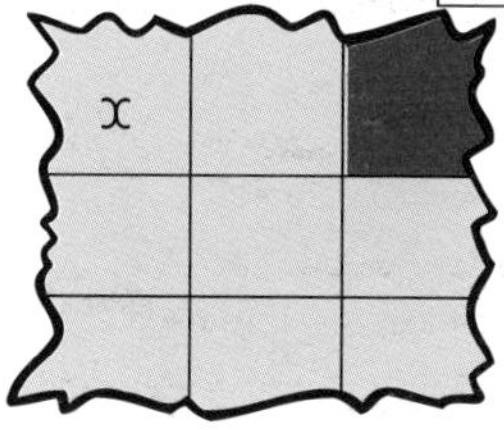

7 x

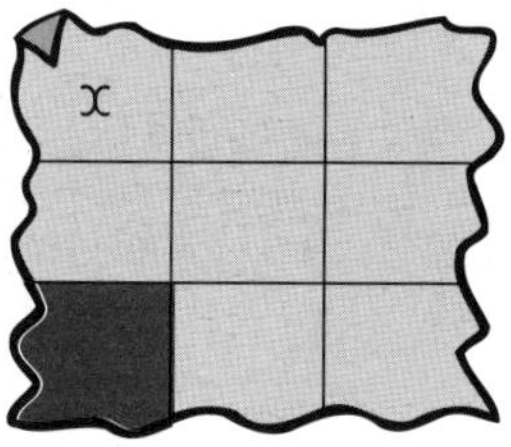

8 x

9 x

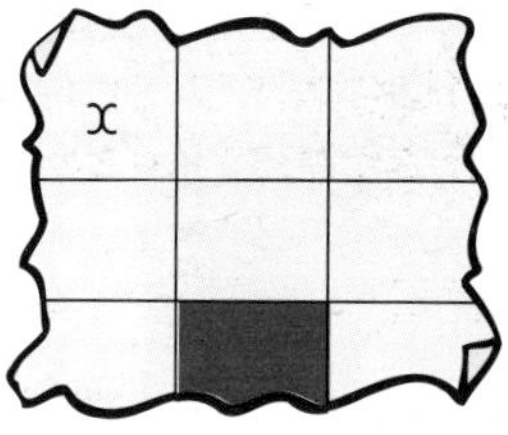

10 x

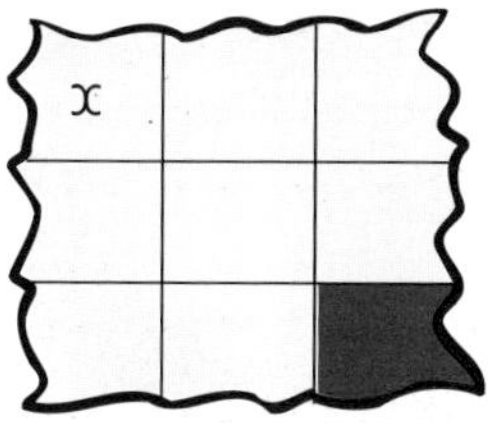

11 x

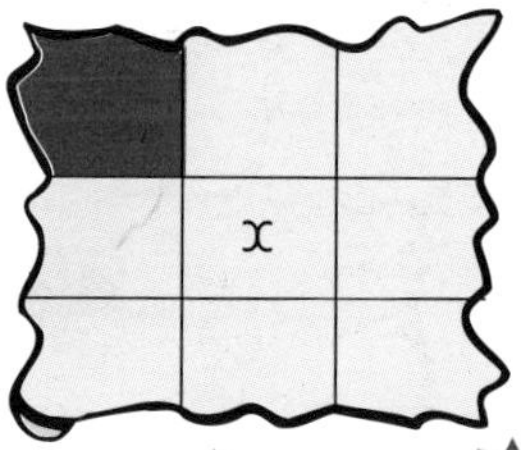

12 x

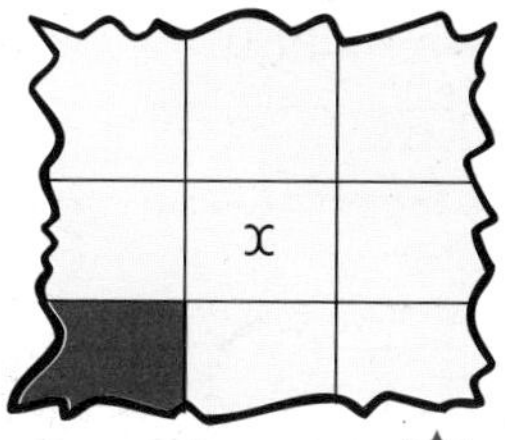

Combine these algebraic terms.

13 $5x + 2x$

14 $7a + 2a$

15 $7c - 3c$

16 $6b - 4b$

17 $5d + d$

18 $e + 7e$

19 $4f - f$

20 $15q + 3q$

21 $2g + 7g$

22 $9y - 3y$

23 $8a + 3a + a$

24 $4x + 7x - x$

25 $2z - z + 3z$

26 $5p - 2p + 3p$

27 $19w - 15w + 9w$

Combining terms

Find the total of the two blue numbers related to y.

M	T	W	T	F	S	S
					1	2
3	4	5	6	7	8	9
10	11	12	13	14	15	16
17	18	19	20	21	22	23
24	25	26	27	28	29	30
31						

1. $y + 1 + y + 7 = 2y + 8$

1 y

2 y

3 y

4 y

5 y

6 y

7 y

8 y

Write the two red numbers on the hundred square related to p, then find their total.

1	2	3	4	5	6	7	8	9	10
11	12	13	14	15	16	17	18	19	20
21	22	23	24	25	26	27	28	29	30
31	32	33	34	35	36	37	38	39	40
41	42	43	44	45	46	47	48	49	50
51	52	53	54	55	56	57	58	59	60
61	62	63	64	65	66	67	68	69	70
71	72	73	74	75	76	77	78	79	80
81	82	83	84	85	86	87	88	89	90
91	92	93	94	95	96	97	98	99	100

?

9 p

10 p

11 p

12 p

13 p

14 p

15 p

Combine these algebraic terms.

?

16	$5c + 3c + 2c$	17	$4x + 3x + 2$	18	$5y - 2y - 4$	19	$3y + 3 + 4y$
20	$2a + 5a - 6$	21	$7b - 3 + 2b$	22	$9 + 3y - y$	23	$10 + 5x - 2x$
24	$3q + 5q + 1$	25	$7t - t - 1$	26	$8m - 5m - m$	27	$3z - z - 2$

Combining terms

Write the perimeter of each shape in terms of the lengths a, b and c.

1

2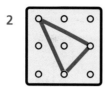

3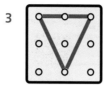

4

5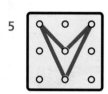

6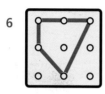

7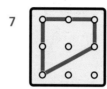

8

9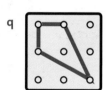

10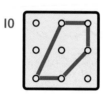

11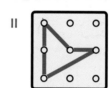

12

Combine these algebraic terms.

13 $3a + 4 + 5a + 2$

14 $6b + 7 + 3b + 1$

?

15 $4y + 2 + 3y - 1$

16 $7z + 3 + 4z - 2$

17 $3p + 5p + 7 - 2p$

18 $5q - 3 + 2q - q$

19 $10c + 3 - 2c - 1$

20 $4t - t + 7 - 2t$

21 $5 + 4m - m - 3$

22 $7 + 8h - 2 - 3h$

23 $6g + 3 + 2g + 7$

24 $5z + 4 + 2y - 1$

25 $3a + b - a + 4$

26 $4w - 3y + 6y - 2$

Explore

Create different pentagons and hexagons using a 3 × 3 geoboard.

Draw them on spotty paper.

Write their perimeters in terms of the lengths a, b and c at the top of the page.

If a = 3, write the value of these expressions.

1 3a

2 5a

3 a + 1

4 3a + 2

5 4a – 1

6 6 – a

7 8 + 2a

8 9 – 2a

9 $\frac{a}{3}$

10 $\frac{a}{2} + 1\frac{1}{2}$

11 a^2

12 $a^2 - 4a$

e Write the value of each expression if a = 5.

Copy and complete the table, substituting the values for x on the left into each expression.

	6x	x + 7	x – 2	4x + 1	5x – 3	$x^2 - 1$
SCREEN 2 x = 4			2			
SCREEN 3 x = 1						
SCREEN 4 x = 10				41		
SCREEN 5 x = 2						3
SCREEN 6 x = 7		14				
SCREEN 7 x = 0	0					

Explore

Create different algebraic expressions involving t, where t = 3.

Each must have a value of 8.

t + 5   14 – 2t

Brackets

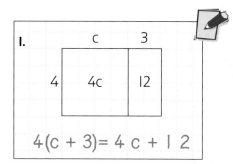

For each multiplication grid, write two equivalent expressions. Use brackets in only one expression.

I.

	c	3
4	4c	12

$4(c + 3) = 4c + 12$

I

	c	3
4		

2

	x	5
3		

3

	y	4
6		

4

	p	2
2		

5

	q	7
q		

Write these expressions without using brackets.

6. $3(a - 2) = 3a - 6$

6	$3(a - 2)$	**7**	$4(c - 1)$	**8**	$2(d + 7)$
9	$5(4 - x)$	**10**	$6(3 + y)$	**11**	$a(b + c)$
12	$2(x + y)$	**13**	$3(b - d)$	**14**	$2(z + \frac{1}{2})$
15	$4(2x + 1)$	**16**	$3(5a - 3)$	**17**	$6(2b - 9)$

Write these expressions using brackets.

18	$5x + 10$	**19**	$2x - 4$	**20**	$4a + 8$
21	$3p - 6$	**22**	$6q + 42$	**23**	$7h - 56$
24	$4g - 4$	**25**	$5p + 5q$	**26**	$2a + 2$
27	$6 + 3d$	**28**	$8 + 2f$	**29**	$4a + 6$

Write the value of each expression if p = 4 and q = 3.

1	p + q	2	p – q	3	2p – q	4	3q + p
5	pq	6	5p – 1	7	3 + 4q	8	4pq
9	3(p + q)	10	5(p – 2)	11	4 (6 – q)	12	2(3p – q)
13	$p^2 + 2q$	14	$q^2 - p$	15	3p – 2q	16	5q – 3p
17	$\frac{p}{2}$	18	$\frac{q}{3}$	19	$\frac{5p}{2}$	20	$\frac{4q}{6}$

e Write the value of each expression if p = 0 and q = 1.

If r = 12, s = 5 and t = 2, find the value of each expression.
Write the capital letters in order to match the value of the
expressions, smallest to largest. What word do you find?

21	**C** rs + t	22	**A** r – st	23	**G** r – s – t
24	**R** r + s + 2t	25	**L** $\frac{r}{s-t}$	26	**I** $\frac{rs}{t}$
27	**A** $s^2 + t^2$	28	**E** $s + \frac{r}{t}$	29	**B** $r^2 - 25s$

Explore

If b = 4 and c = 5, create
different algebraic expressions
involving b and c.

They must each have a value of 20.

5c – b – 1

2b + 2c + 2

Formulae

l

w

length → l
width → w
Area → A
Perimeter → P

$$A = lw$$
$$P = 2(l + w)$$

Use the formulae for rectangles to solve these problems.

1
l = 8 cm
w = 4·5 cm
Find area.

2
A = 18 cm^2
w = 8 cm
Find length.

3
A = 36 m^2
l = 12 m
Find width.

4
l = 9 cm
w = 3·5 cm
Find perimeter.

5
P = 56 cm
w = 11 cm
Find length.

6
P = 34 m
l = 10·5 m
Find width.

7
P = 28 cm
l = 9 cm
Find area.

8
A = 48 m^2
w = 6 m
Find perimeter.

h

b

h

b

base → b
height → h
Area → A

$$A = \frac{hb}{2}$$

Use the formula for triangles to solve these problems.

9
h = 5 cm
b = 4 cm
Find area.

10
A = 21 cm^2
h = 7 cm
Find base.

11
A = 27 m^2
b = 6 m
Find height.

Problems

12 An isosceles right-angled triangle has an area of 40·5 cm^2. What length are its equal sides?

13 The perpendicular sides of a right-angled triangle are in the ratio of 2:1. What are the lengths of these sides if its area is 9 cm^2?

Use these formulae to find the values of the unknown capital letters.

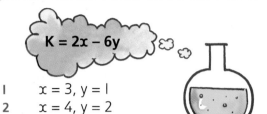

K = 2x − 6y

1   $x = 3, y = 1$
2   $x = 4, y = 2$
3   $x = 6, y = 1$

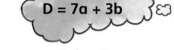

D = 7a + 3b

4   $a = 2, b = 1$
5   $a = 3, b = 6$
6   $a = 0.5, b = 1.5$

$$P = \frac{100}{ab}$$

7   $a = 4, b = 5$
8   $a = 5, b = 10$
9   $a = 3, b = 20$

$$Z = \frac{(a+b)}{2}$$

10   $a = 11, b = 7$
11   $a = 4, b = 9$
12   $a = 1.2, b = 0.6$

$$T = \frac{n(n+1)}{2}$$

13   $n = 7$
14   $n = 10$
15   $n = 1$

$$G = \frac{x}{2} + 7t$$

16   $x = 4, t = 3$
17   $x = 18, t = 2$
18   $x = 13, t = 0.5$

℮   Write numbers that the small letters could be so that each capital letter equals 1.

One English pound (P) is approximately $2\frac{1}{2}$ Australian dollars (d). These can be connected by the formula $d = \frac{5p}{2}$.

Find how many dollars you can exchange for: 19   £10   20   £14   21   £9

Find how many pounds you can exchange for: 22 $20   23 $15   24 $30

Temperature in degrees Celcius (C) and degrees Fahrenheit (F) are connected by the formula $F = \frac{9C}{5} + 32$.

25   15°C   26   20°C   27   5°C

Find these temperatures in degrees Fahrenheit.

Write a formula to calculate:

1 the number of months (m) in y years

2 the number of weeks (w) in d days

3 the number of hours (h) in d days

4 the number of hours (h) in m minutes

5 the number of centimetres (c) in m metres

6 the number of grams (g) in k kilograms

7 the number of vertices (v) in h hexagons and s squares

8 the number of wheels (w) on t tricycles and b bicycles

9 the number of legs (l) on c chairs and s stools

Count the number of black and white squares in each rectangle.

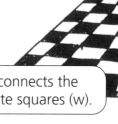

For each set of rectangles, write a formula which connects the number of black squares (b) to the number of white squares (w).

10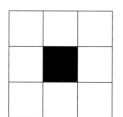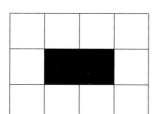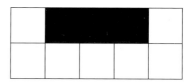

11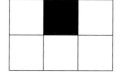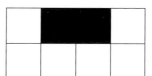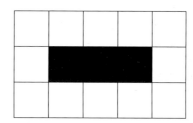

12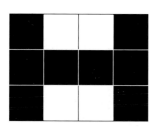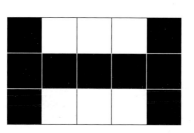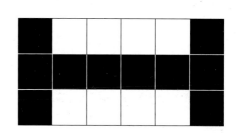

Equations

Solve these equations.

1	$x + 4 = 10$	2	$y + 7 = 15$	3	$12 = z + 1$	4	$21 = p + 14$
5	$5 + q = 13$	6	$25 = 17 + p$	7	$a - 3 = 9$	8	$13 = b - 6$
9	$15 - d = 9$	10	$8 = 17 - f$	11	$g - 4 = 18$	12	$16 = f - 2$
13	$9 = 18 - y$	14	$14 + x = 16$	15	$27 = m - 3$	16	$m + 21 = 38 - 2$
17	$48 - p = 16 + 3$	18	$12 + q = 45 - 30$	19	$15 + 21 = 47 - s$	20	$81 - 49 = t + 11$

Write an equation for each puzzle, then solve it.

I think of a number ...

21 ... then add 6. My answer is 13.

22 ... then subtract 14. My answer is 9.

23 ... then add it to 7. My answer is 21.

24 ... then subtract it from 16. My answer is 9.

25 ... then add 19. My answer is 47.

26 ... then subtract 19. My answer is 36.

27 ... then add it to 15. My answer is 71.

28 ... then subtract it from 100. My answer is 83.

ℯ Invent four of your own 'Think of a number' puzzles. Write an equation and the solution for each. Try them out on a friend.

Explore

Invent different equations using y, where y = 5 is the solution.

For example, $2y + 1 = 11$.

Can you write ten different equations?

Use different operations, brackets and squares.

Equations

$$2y = 12$$
$$4p = 16$$
$$9x = 36$$

Solve these equations.

1	$2y = 12$	2	$5z = 30$	3	$7p = 49$
4	$64 = 4q$	5	$88 = 11z$	6	$36 = 2h$
7	$3p = 27$	8	$54 = 6g$	9	$9m = 72$
10	$56 = 7y$	11	$4t = 48$	12	$96 = 8n$

Solve these.

13	$2x - 1 = 7$	14	$2a + 3 = 11$	15	$3z - 2 = 7$
16	$4h + 3 = 23$	17	$5y + 4 = 39$	18	$6g + 8 = 32$
19	$50 = 9p + 5$	20	$29 = 2q + 5$	21	$7t - 4 = 59$
22	$8d - 7 = 33$	23	$29 = 4p - 3$	24	$18 = 3b - 9$

Find the mystery numbers. Write an equation for each, then solve it.

25 If I multiply the number by 4, then subtract 7, the answer is 1.

26 If I treble the number, and add 1, the answer is 13.

27 If I add 15 to double the number, the answer is 29.

28 If I multiply the number by 4, then subtract it from 18, the answer is 10.

29 Eleven times the number added to 5 is the same as 7 squared.

30 If I multiply the number by 8, then subtract 8, the answer is two dozen.

Arithmogons

Copy the arithmogons, then write the missing numbers in the squares.

The number in each square is the total of the two numbers in the circles on either side.

1
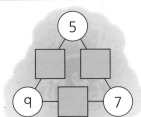

(5)
□ □
(9)—□—(7)

2
(14)
□ □
(13)—□—(9)

3
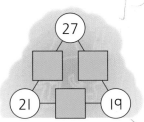
(27)
□ □
(21)—□—(19)

Use algebra to find the mystery numbers in the circles.

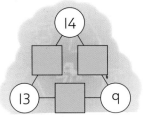

Let one circle number be x.

4.
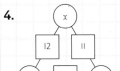

(x)
| 12 | | 11 |
(12 − x)—| 15 |—(11 − x)

(4)
| 12 | | 11 |
(8)—| 15 |—(7)

$$15 = 12 − x + 11 − x$$
$$15 = 23 − 2x$$
$$2x = 8$$
$$x = 4$$

4
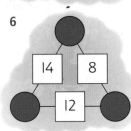
| 12 | | 11 |
| 15 |

5
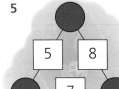
| 5 | | 8 |
| 7 |

6
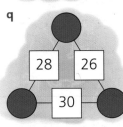
| 14 | | 8 |
| 12 |

7
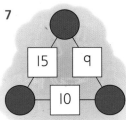
| 15 | | 9 |
| 10 |

8
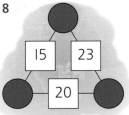
| 15 | | 23 |
| 20 |

9
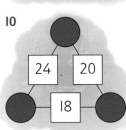
| 28 | | 26 |
| 30 |

10
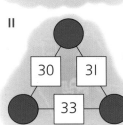
| 24 | | 20 |
| 18 |

11

| 30 | | 31 |
| 33 |

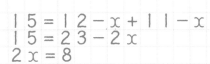

Explore

Find as many different solutions as you can to these square arithmogons.

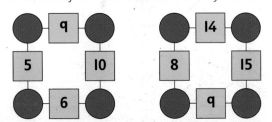

○ | 9 | ○
| 5 | | 10 |
○ | 6 | ○

○ | 14 | ○
| 8 | | 15 |
○ | 9 | ○

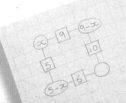

Straight-line graphs

For each set of points, draw the first quadrant of a coordinate grid. Plot the points and join them with a straight line.

Write the equation of each line.

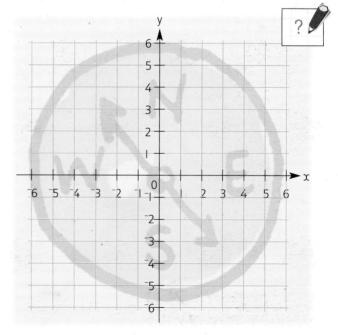

I	(1,3)	**2**	(4,2)	**3**	(3,3)
	(5,3)		(4,4)		(4,4)
	(8,3)		(4,0)		(0,0)
	(0,3)		(4,8)		(8,8)

4	(4,5)	**5**	(5,3)	**6**	(2,4)
	(7,8)		(2,0)		(4,8)
	(0,1)		(8,6)		(3,6)
	(2,3)		(3,1)		(1,2)

     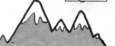

For each set of points, draw a four-quadrant coordinate grid. Plot the points and join them with a straight line.

Write the equation of each line.

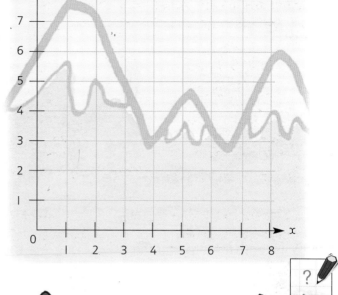

7	(4,¯2)	**8**	(¯4,3)	**q**	(5,4)
	(0,¯2)		(¯4,¯4)		(0,¯1)
	(¯3,¯2)		(¯4,0)		(3,2)
	(¯5,¯2)		(¯4,¯1)		(1,0)

10	(¯3,0)	**II**	(¯5,¯4)	**12**	(0,0)
	(0,3)		(¯1,0)		(2,6)
	(¯5,¯2)		(2,3)		(¯1,¯3)
	(1,4)		(4,5)		(1,3)

Straight-line graphs

Name the points which lie on these lines.

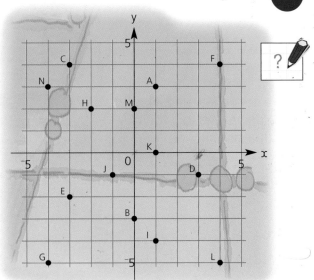

1	$y = 2$	**2**	$y = {}^-1$
3	$x = 4$	**4**	$y = 3$
5	$x = {}^-3$	**6**	$x = 1$
7	$y = {}^-5$	**8**	$x = 0$
9	$x = {}^-4$	**10**	$y = {}^-4$

Use the equations to find the value of y for each value of x.

Complete the pairs of coordinates.

11.

x	0	1	2	5
	+ 2	+ 2	+ 2	+ 2
y	2	3	4	7

(0,2), (1,3), (2,4), (5,7)

11 $y = x + 2$ (0,) (1,) (2,) (5,)

12 $y = x - 3$ (3,) (5,) (1,) (9,)

13 $y = 3x - 1$ (2,) (1,) (4,) (0,)

14 $y = 4 + x$ (3,) (2,) (⁻3,) (⁻1,)

15 $y = 2x - 3$ (2,) (5,) (3,) (0,)

16 $y = 6x$ (2,) (5,) (4,) (0,)

17 $y = \frac{1}{2}x$ (4,) (8,) (12,) (2,)

Write four points which lie on each line.

18 $y = 2x + 1$ **19** $y = 3x$ **20** $y = x - 6$

21 $y = 5x - 2$ **22** $y = x$ **23** $y = 3x - 4$

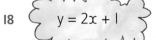

Straight-line graphs

Write the equation of each red line.

1
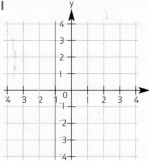

2
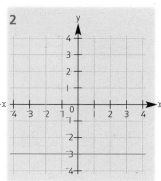

3
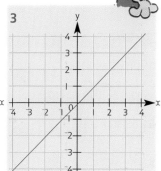

4
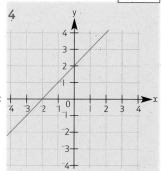

Draw the first quadrant of a coordinate grid.

Plot the lines with these equations. What do you notice?

5 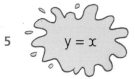 $y = x$

6 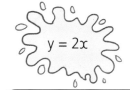 $y = 2x$

7 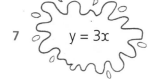 $y = 3x$

8 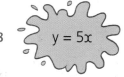 $y = 5x$

Draw a four-quadrant coordinate grid.

Plot the lines with these equations. What do you notice?

9 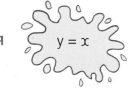 $y = x$

10  $y = x + 1$

11  $y = x + 4$

12 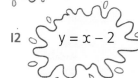 $y = x - 2$

13 $y = x - 6$

Explore

Find some points that fit the equation $y + x = 6$.

Plot them on a coordinate grid.

What do you notice?

Explore different lines of this type, e.g. $y + x = 0$, $y + x = 3$, $y + x = 5$, ...

Write what you notice about all the lines.

Interpret each graph by answering the questions.

1 How long did the journey take?

2 How far away from home is the shop?

3 For how long did Carol stop at the shop?

4 For how long was she walking?

5 Did she walk quicker going to the shop or coming back?

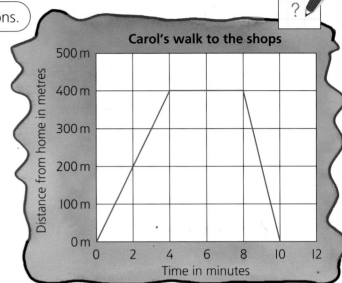

Carol's walk to the shops

Distance from home in metres / Time in minutes

6 How far did the Smith family travel?

7 How long did it take?

8 How many stops were there on the way?

9 How far did they travel between 1 o'clock and 3 o'clock?

10 Which stage of the journey was the quickest?

11 What was the average distance travelled per hour for the whole journey (including the stop)?

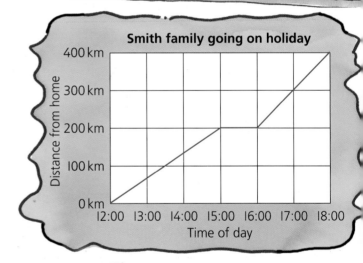

Smith family going on holiday

Distance from home / Time of day

12 How far is the cinema from home?

13 How long did Gary's journey take?

14 For how long did Gary stop on his way back?

15 Which stage of the journey, apart from the stops, was the slowest?

16 For how long was Gary on the move?

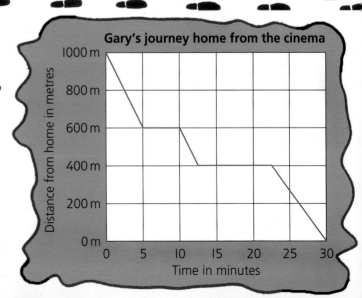

Gary's journey home from the cinema

Distance from home in metres / Time in minutes

Graphs

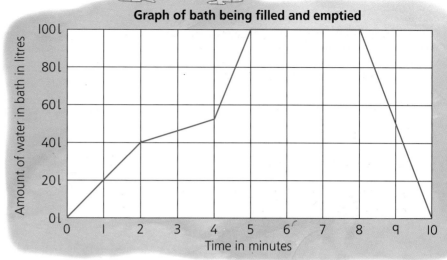

Graph of bath being filled and emptied

Write a description of the bath being filled and emptied.

The graph shows the journeys of two friends who like cycling. They live 50 km apart and decide to swap houses for a few days' holiday. They both set off at 9:00 a.m. and cycle to each other's house.

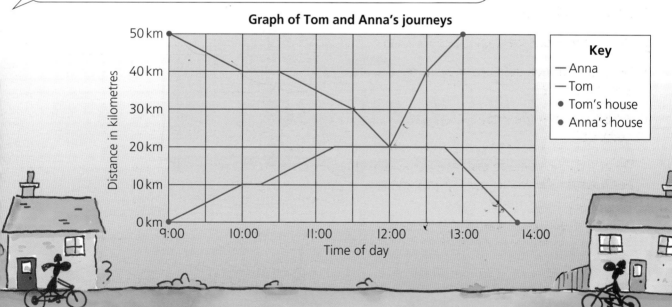

Graph of Tom and Anna's journeys

Key
— Anna
— Tom
● Tom's house
● Anna's house

1 How long did it take for Anna to cycle to Tom's house?

2 How far had Anna travelled at 11:30? How far at 12:30?

3 How long did it take for Tom to cycle to Anna's house?

4 How far had Tom travelled at 11:30? How far at 13:30?

5 At what time did they meet?

6 At what time had Tom completed two fifths of his journey?

7 How far had each travelled when they met?

8 At what time had Anna finished four fifths of her journey?

9 For how long altogether did Anna stop?

10 Who had travelled the furthest by 12:00?

11 For how long altogether did Tom stop?

12 At approximately what time did each reach the half-way stage of their journey?

Draw a graph to match each story.

1 Sally ran 200 m steadily in 2 minutes, rested for 1 minute, then walked back in 4 minutes.

2 Kerry cycled 1000 m to the cycle repair shop in 10 minutes. Three minutes later he left the shop and walked back home at a steady pace. It took him 15 minutes to get home.

3 John travelled home from his friend's house, which is 50 miles away. He caught a bus at 9 o'clock which took him 10 miles in 1 hour. He waited for 1 hour at the station, then caught a train which took him the next 20 miles in half an hour. He waited for half an hour at the station, then caught another train which took him 15 miles in 1 hour. Finally, he cycled the remaining distance home. He arrived at 2 o'clock in the afternoon.

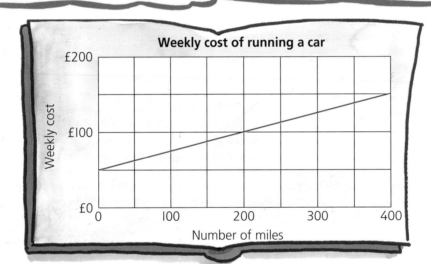

Weekly cost of running a car

Weekly cost / Number of miles

The graph shows the weekly cost of running a car. Use the graph to find the cost of running the car if the driver travels:

4 100 miles
5 300 miles
6 250 miles
7 180 miles

How many miles will the driver have travelled in a week if the cost is:

8 £100?
9 £75?
10 £150?
11 £120?

🌍 Write how many kilometres the driver will have travelled.

Explore

Draw your own distance-time graph to describe a journey.

Invent a story to match the graph.

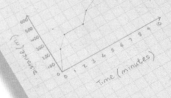

Function machines

Write what happens to these numbers when each rule is applied to them.

4 **7**

10

Ia. $x = 4$
$3x - 1 = 11$

I

$3x - 1$ Treble it, then subtract 1.

2

$2(x + 1)$ Add 1, then double it.

3

$10x - 3$ Multiply by 10, then subtract 3.

4

$4x + 7$ Multiply by 4, then add 7.

5

$x^2 + 2$ Square it, then add 2.

6

$5x + 7$ Multiply by 5, then add 7.

For each twin function machine, copy and complete the table.

in	I	2	3	4	5
out					

7  multiply by 2 — add I

8 multiply by 3 — subtract I

9 multiply by 4 — subtract 3

10 double it — add 3

II add I — treble it

12 square it — subtract I

13 subtract I — multiply by 5

14 add 6 — subtract 3

Describe each twin function machine using algebra. What is the effect of the machine on an unknown number x?

7a. $x \rightarrow 2x + 1$

79

Write the input number for each function machine.

1 | add 3 | multiply by 2 | **14**

2 | add 4 | multiply by 3 | **30**

3 | subtract 4 | multiply by 3 | **9**

4 | multiply by 2 | subtract 1 | **5**

5 | multiply by 3 | subtract 5 | **10**

6 | multiply by 5 | subtract 3 | **42**

7 | square it | add 3 | **7**

8 | multiply by 10 | subtract 7 | **73**

9 | add 1 | square it | **49**

10 | cube it | subtract 5 | **22**

For each puzzle, draw a twin function machine to help you find the mystery number.

11 I'm thinking of a number. If I double it, then add 3, the answer is 17.

12 I'm thinking of a number. If I treble it, then subtract 4, the answer is 11.

13 I'm thinking of a number. If I add 6, then multiply by 5, the answer is 45.

14 I'm thinking of a number. If I subtract 3, then multiply by 4, the answer is 20.

15 I'm thinking of a number. If I square it, then subtract 7, the answer is 9.

16 I'm thinking of a number. If I subtract 2, then square it, the answer is 25.

Copy and complete this table for each of these functions.

in	1	2	3	4	5	6	7	8
out								

1   $x \rightarrow 2x + 5$

2   $x \rightarrow 3x - 1$

3   $x \rightarrow 8 - x$

4   $x \rightarrow 4 + 3x$

5   $x \rightarrow 100 - 9x$

6   $x \rightarrow x^2 + 1$

7   $x \rightarrow \frac{x}{2} + 3$

8   $x \rightarrow x^2 + \frac{x}{2}$

(11)   (7)   (24)   (13)   (44)   (27)   (2)   (17)   (31)

For each machine, find the mystery function. Write the function, then fill in the missing numbers in the table.

9   add 1

in	out
2	5
5	11
4	9
7	15
3	
6	
8	
10	

10   minus 1

in	out
4	11
8	23
2	5
6	17
3	
7	
1	
5	

11   multiply by 5

in	out
10	43
5	18
7	28
8	33
4	
9	
6	
3	

12   add 1

in	out
9	82
6	37
5	26
7	50
10	
3	
8	
2	

13   add 20

in	out
4	12
7	6
3	14
5	10
2	
9	
6	
8	

14   minus 1

in	out
1	0
3	4
5	16
7	36
4	
8	
2	
6	

Sequences

> Continue these sequences to the tenth term.

1
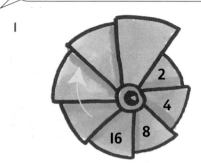
2, 4, 8, 16

2

68, 73, 63

3
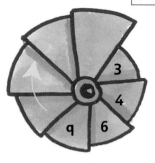
3, 4, 6, 9

4
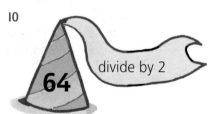
2, 4, 8

5

1, 4, 9, 16

6
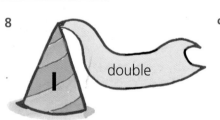
3, 6, 24

> Write the first six terms of these sequences. Start at the numbers given and use the rules shown.

7. 2, 5, 8, 11, ...

7
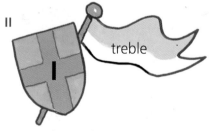
2 — add 3

8
1 — double

9
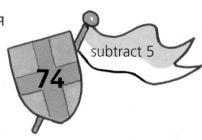
74 — subtract 5

10
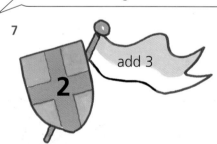
64 — divide by 2

11
1 — treble

12
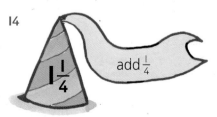
2 — multiply by 10

13
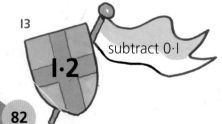
1·2 — subtract 0·1

14
$1\frac{1}{4}$ — add $\frac{1}{4}$

Sequences

Each of these sequences has a rule involving adding or subtracting only. Write the first six numbers of each sequence.

1

start	5th term
2	10

2

start	4th term
5	17

3

start	4th term
56	41

4

start	4th term
0·3	1·05

5

start	6th term
7	37

6

start	3rd term
90	64

e Describe the rule for each sequence.

Write the number of matchsticks used to make each shape. Write the number of matchsticks needed for the next three shapes in each sequence.

7

8

9

10

11

Describe the rule for each sequence.

Write the first six terms of these sequences. Start at the number given and use the rule shown.

I. 4 1 2, 2 8, 6 0, ...

1

4 — add 2, then double

2

3 — subtract 1, then double

3

2 — double, then subtract 1

4

156 — halve, then subtract 2

5

4 — multiply by 6, then halve

6

$\frac{1}{4}$ — double, then add $\frac{1}{2}$

7

0·14 — multiply by 10, then subtract 1

8

2 — multiply by 3, then add 1

9

2 — add 0·1, then double

10

1 — subtract 0·3, then double

Explore

Sequences can make number chains.

> **Rule:** If the number is even, halve it.
> If the number is odd, multiply by 3, then add 1.

Continue this chain starting at 6: **6 → 3 → 10 → 5 → 16 ...**

Describe what happens.

Explore chains made using this rule and starting with other numbers.

Put all the chains together on one diagram.

The nth term

Write these rules for shape number n.

I. 6 n

I 6 times the shape number

2 double the shape number, then add 1

3 treble the shape number, then subtract 2

4 10 times the shape number, then add 1

5 5 times the shape number, then subtract 6

6 halve the shape number, then add 3

7 multiply the shape number by itself, then subtract 3

Write how many sticks are needed to make the tenth shape in each sequence.

?

8

9

10

11

12

13

14

15

16

17

ℯ Write the rule for shape number n in each sequence.

The nth term

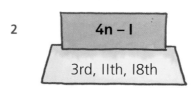

Write these terms for each sequence.

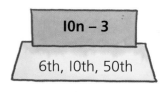

I.	$3n + 7$
a.	$(3 \times 4) + 7 = 19$

1
3n + 7
4th, 15th, 21st

2
4n − 1
3rd, 11th, 18th

3
10n − 3
6th, 10th, 50th

4
6n + 4
4th, 8th, 15th

5
$n^2 + 4$
4th, 6th, 10th

6
$\frac{n}{2} + 5$
4th, 18th, 23rd

Describe the rules in words to show the relationship between the numbers and the terms for each sequence. Write the nth term for each.

7

Term	1	2	3	4	n
Number	2	4	6	8	

8

Term	1	2	3	4	n
Number	10	20	30	40	

9

Term	1	2	3	4	n
Number	3	5	7	9	

10

Term	1	2	3	4	n
Number	4	7	10	13	

11

Term	1	2	3	4	n
Number	13	23	33	43	

12

Term	1	2	3	4	n
Number	4	8	12	16	

13

Term	1	2	3	4	n
Number	2	5	8	11	

14

Term	1	2	3	4	n
Number	3	8	13	18	

For each set of shapes, write a sequence for the number of lines, then the number of spots.

Write the number of lines and spots in the nth shape.

Ia. $2n + 1$
Ib. $n + 2$

1

2

3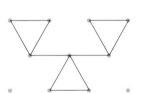

4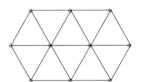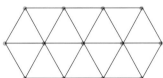

5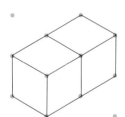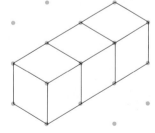

Explore

Look at this sequence of totals.

$1 + 2 = \mathbf{3}$
$1 + 2 + 3 = \mathbf{6}$
$1 + 2 + 3 + 4 = \mathbf{10}$

Show that the nth term (total) will be $\frac{n}{2}(n + 1)$.

Find the total of the first ten counting numbers, i.e. $1 + 2 + \ldots + 10$. Use the rule to check.

Find the total of the numbers on a 1 to 100 grid.

Weight and capacity

Copy and complete these.

1	3000 ml = ☁ l		2	4·6 l = ☁ ml		3	430 cl = ☁ l
4	650 ml = ☁ cl		5	75 cl = ☁ l		6	0·56 l = ☁ ml
7	1·23 l.= ☁ cl		8	2 l = ☁ cm³		9	325 cm³ = ☁ cl
10	180 cm³ = ☁ ml		11	0·8 l = ☁ cm³		12	3·5 gallons = ☁ pints
13	20 pints = ☁ gallons		14	100 pints = ☁ l		15	35 cl = ☁ cm³

Write an estimated order for each set of capacities, smallest to largest.

Convert each capacity into litres. Write the correct order and compare it with your estimated order.

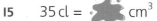

16   46 cl   650 ml   0·53 l   1·6 l   ¼ gallon   1½ pints

17   ½ gallon   250 cl   2400 ml   2·3 l   6 pints   300 cl

ℓ Convert each capacity into cubic centimetres.

Write which units you would use to measure these.

18   weight of a book

19   weight of a lorry

20   capacity of a car's petrol tank

21   weight of a coin

22   amount of liquid in a cup of tea

23   your weight

24   amount of water in a swimming pool

Choose the appropriate measure for these.

25	weight of an egg			26	amount of cola in a can			27	weight of a packet of crisps		
	0·5 oz	50 g	0·75 kg		80 cl	1·5 l	350 ml		1 lb	30 g	100 g

Weight and capacity

> Copy and complete these.

1 426 g =  kg

2 0·47 kg = g

3 700 g = kg

4 3500 kg = tonnes

5 2·6 tonnes = kg

6 70 g = kg

7 9 g = kg

8 3 lb = oz

9 0·5 lb = oz

10 40 oz = lb

11 100 lb = kg

12 2·5 kg = lb

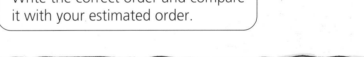

> Write an estimated order for the weights in each set, smallest to largest.

> Write each weight in kilograms. Write the correct order and compare it with your estimated order.

13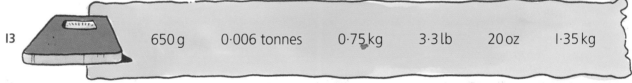

650 g   0·006 tonnes   0·75 kg   3·3 lb   20 oz   1·35 kg

14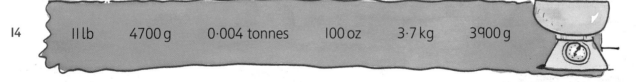

11 lb   4700 g   0·004 tonnes   100 oz   3·7 kg   3900 g

e Write each weight in grams.

Explore

Cubes with sides 1 cm long are placed in a 10 × 10 tray.

How many cubes are needed to fill the tray?

How many cubes are needed for two trays? Three trays?
Continue to find how many cubes are needed to fill ten trays.

If 1 cm³ = 1 ml, find how many cubic centimetres are in one litre.

Weight and capacity problems

1 A bag of potatoes contains 5·5 kg. Brian uses 650 g to cook dinner. How many kilograms of potatoes are left?

2 A tin of soup weighs 425 g. What is the weight of 5 tins in kilograms?

3 The corner shop sells sweets at 24p per ounce. The supermarket sells the same sweets at 85p per 100 g. Which is the best value?

4 The supermarket sells cheese at £3·18 per kilogram. The same cheese is for sale on a market stall for £1·50 per pound. Which is cheaper?

5 The contents of a jar of cooking sauce weighs 375 g. The recipe says add 0·5 kg of chicken and 150 g of onions. What is the total weight of the ingredients in kilograms?

6 Mike buys 6 pints of milk for £2·10 at one shop and 3 litres of milk for £1·80 at another. Which is cheaper?

7 A garage sells petrol for 76p per litre. Simon spends £14·06 on petrol. How many litres does he buy?

8 As a prize in supermarket competition Nina can choose to have a 5 lb box of chocolates, a 6000 g bar of chocolate, 3·75 kg of chocolate, or 100 oz of chocolates. Write which should she choose and why.

Surface area

Calculate the surface areas of these cuboids.

1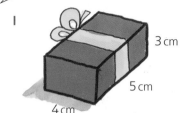
3 cm
5 cm
4 cm

2 2 cm 3 cm
8 cm

3 8 cm   9 cm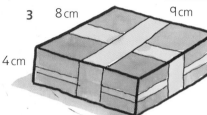
4 cm

4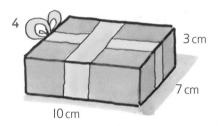
3 cm
7 cm
10 cm

5 15 cm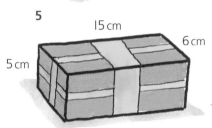
6 cm
5 cm

6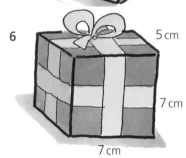
5 cm
7 cm
7 cm

Use cubes with sides 1 cm long to make these models.

Find the surface area of each model.

7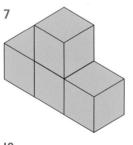

8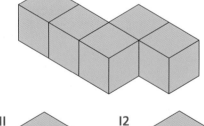

9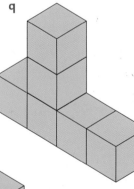

10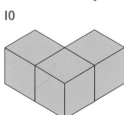

11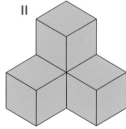

12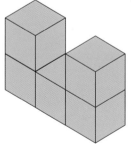

Explore

Make models by joining cubes together.

How many different models can you build using two cubes?

How many using three cubes? Four cubes? …

Investigate the surface areas of your models.

Surface area

Calculate the surface areas of these shapes.

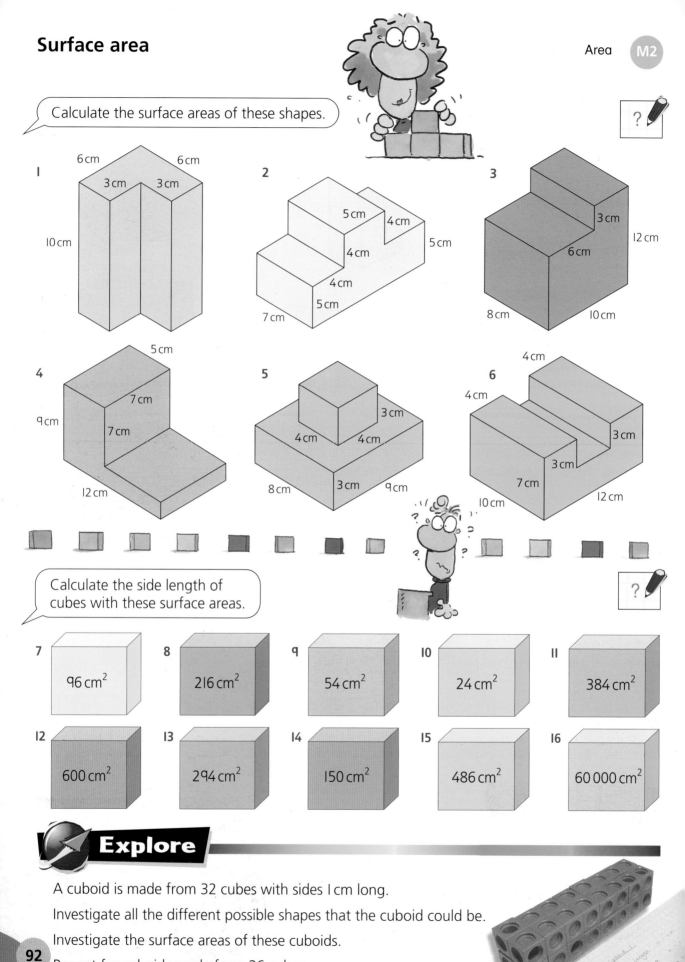

1
6 cm   6 cm
3 cm   3 cm
10 cm

2
5 cm   4 cm
4 cm   5 cm
4 cm
5 cm
7 cm

3
3 cm
12 cm
6 cm
8 cm   10 cm

4
5 cm
7 cm
9 cm
7 cm
12 cm

5
3 cm
4 cm   4 cm
8 cm   3 cm   9 cm

6
4 cm
4 cm
3 cm
3 cm
7 cm
10 cm   12 cm

Calculate the side length of
cubes with these surface areas.

7 96 cm²

8 216 cm²

9 54 cm²

10 24 cm²

11 384 cm²

12 600 cm²

13 294 cm²

14 150 cm²

15 486 cm²

16 60 000 cm²

Explore

A cuboid is made from 32 cubes with sides 1 cm long.

Investigate all the different possible shapes that the cuboid could be.

Investigate the surface areas of these cuboids.

Repeat for cuboids made from 36 cubes.

Find the surface area of this red cuboid.

30 cm   20 cm

60 cm

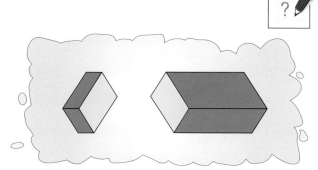

The cuboid is cut into two along a line 10 cm from the top face. Find the surface area of the two new cuboids.

What is the ratio of the total yellow surface area to the total red surface area?

Find the surface area of each of these cuboid-shaped cakes.

1

10 cm   28 cm

10 cm

2

22 cm

7 cm

16 cm

3

11 Today

20 cm   34 cm

14 cm

e Find the surface area of cuboids with side lengths double these.
Then find the surface area of cuboids with side lengths treble these.

Explore

A cube has side length l.

Find a formula for the surface area of a cube.

Check using cubes of different sizes.

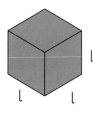

l

l   l

side length = l

Area

Calculate the areas of these triangles.

1   4 cm   6 cm

2   8 cm   3·6 cm

3   5 cm   9 cm

4   4·8 cm   6 cm

5   10 cm   6·8 cm

6   12 cm   11·8 cm

7   4 cm   3·4 cm

8   13·2 cm   8 cm

Write the missing measurements for these right-angled triangles.

9   h = 5 cm, b = 6 cm, A =

10   A = 300 cm^2, b = 20 cm, h =

11   h = 4 cm, A = 14 cm^2, b =

12   A = 16·8 cm^2, b = 8 cm, h =

13   A = 70 cm^2, h = 10 cm, b =

14   b = 6·2 cm, A = 15·5 cm, h =

15   isosceles right-angled triangle,
     A = 72 cm^2, h =   , b =

16   isosceles right-angled triangle,
     A = 32 cm^2, h =   , b =

Calculate the areas of these shapes.

17   5 cm   4 cm   10 cm

18   5 cm   11·8 cm   6 cm   8 cm

19   8 cm   6 cm   7 cm

20   3 cm   5 cm   3 cm   10 cm

21   9 cm   5 cm   5 cm   8 cm   5 cm   5 cm

22   10 cm   10 cm   11 cm   16 cm

Area

Calculate the areas of these school playing fields in hectares.

1

400 m
800 m
500 m
1000 m

2

180 m
350 m
150 m
420 m

3

650 m
250 m
150 m
450 m

4

90 m
145 m
60 m
310 m

SCHOOL BUS

Use cm-squared paper and plot these points on a coordinate grid.

Join the points to create shapes, then calculate the area of each.

5 (1,1), (1,3), (3,3)

6 (⁻5,4), (⁻5,1), (0,4)

7 (0,⁻2), (2,⁻2), (5,1), (3,1)

8 (6,⁻1), (6,⁻5), (2,⁻5), (2,⁻3)

9 (⁻1,⁻1), (⁻4,⁻1), (⁻5,⁻4), (0,⁻4)

Explore

There are 16 different quadrilaterals which can be constructed on a 3 × 3 geoboard.

Can you find them all? Check that none are congruent.

Calculate the area of each quadrilateral in units^2.

How many have area of 0·5 units^2, 1 unit^2, 1·5 units^2, 2 units^2, ... ?

Area problems

1 A rectangular playground is 45·7 m long and 38·2 m wide. What is its area?

2 The school hall is rectangular and has an area of 851 m². If it is 37 m long, calculate its width.

3 The school garden is a rectangle 22 m long and 18·5 m wide. It has a triangular flower bed 13·2 m long and 7·5 m high. The rest is a grass lawn. What is the area of the lawn?

4 A football tournament is held on a large rectangular playing field which is 650 m long and 375 m wide. In the corner of the playing field a rectangular area 75 m long and 60 m wide is used as a car park. What is the area of the playing field that can be used for football?

5 The school hall is 52 m long and 47 m wide. In the centre of the hall stage blocks cover an area 133 m². What area of the hall is left for seating?

6 The new classroom carpet costs £23·50 per square metre. The classroom is a rectangle 14·5 m long and 11·8 m wide. Carpet is sold to the nearest square metre. How much does the carpet cost?

7 The Year 6 classroom is to have new floor tiles everywhere except in the painting area. The classroom is 13·8 m long and 11·7 m wide. The painting area covers 9·6 m². What area of the classroom will have new floor tiles?

8 A new car park is being built at the front of the school. It is 66 m long and 27 m wide. Part of the car park will be used to build a bike shed 5 m wide and 8 m long. Calculate the area left for parking cars.

Lines and angles

Use isometric (spotty) paper and copy each diagram.

Colour equal angles. Use one colour for all angles which are the same size.

1   **2**   **3**   **4**

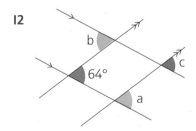

Write the angles marked with letters.

5

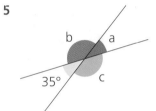

b   a   35°   c

6

130°   a

b

c

7

65°   a   b   c

8

108°   c   a   b

9

b   a   c   66°

10

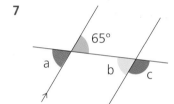

a   95°   b   c   125°

11

68°   c   a   b   81°

12

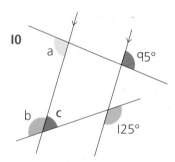

b   64°   c   a

13

110°   40°   c   b   a

14

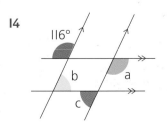

116°   b   a   c

15

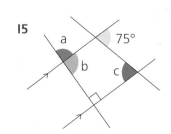

a   75°   b   c

Angles of a triangle

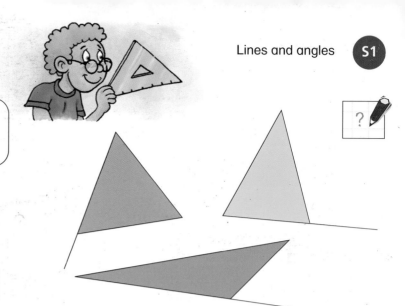

Draw three large triangles on paper. Extend one side of each triangle to create an exterior angle.

Use your protractor to measure the exterior angle and the three interior angles of each triangle.

Write what you notice about any relationships between the angles.

Write the angles marked with letters.

1

a
54° 108°

2
115°
72°
b

3
64°
c
76°

4
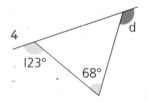
123°
68°
d

5
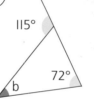
162°
32° e

6
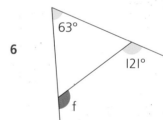
63°
121°
f

7
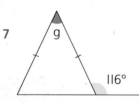
g
116°

8
136°
h

9

71°
i

Explore

Copy this diagram.

Use different colours to mark equal angles.

Write why these angles are equal.

Explain how your diagram shows a relationship between the size of the exterior angle and the size of the opposite interior angles.

Coordinates

Join each set of points, in order, to create a shape. Write the name of each shape.

1   (1,4), (1,6), (⁻3,6)

2   (⁻5,⁻5), (1,⁻3), (1,⁻6)

3   (2,5), (⁻2,4), (⁻1,0), (3,1)

4   (⁻2,0), (0,2), (4,⁻2), (2,⁻4)

5   (1,2), (4,3), (4,⁻1), (1,⁻2)

6   (⁻6,2), (⁻6,4), (⁻4,4), (0,0)

7   (⁻3,1), (⁻5,⁻3), (⁻3,⁻1), (⁻1,⁻3)

8   (3,⁻3), (2,⁻6), (6,⁻6), (5,⁻3)

Write the coordinates of the mid-points of these sides.

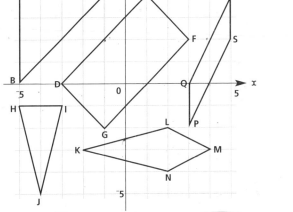

9   AC

10   QR

11   HI

12   DE

13   KL

14   HJ

15   BC

16   QR

17   RS

18   EF

19   NM

20   GF

21   DG

22   AB

23   SP

24   IJ

25   LM

26   KN

Draw a congruent shape to each of these and write its coordinates.

27

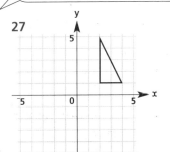

28

29

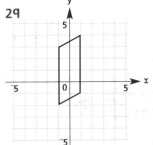

30

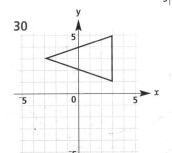

31

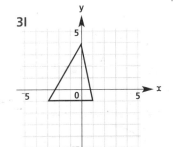

32

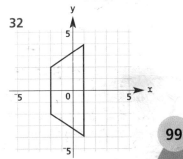

Coordinates

Each shape has a missing coordinate. Plot the points given, then write the coordinates of the missing point.

1 square (0,4), (⁻3,5), (⁻4,2)

2 arrowhead (⁻1,⁻4), (5,⁻2), (3,⁻4)

3 parallelogram (⁻6,⁻3), (⁻4,⁻1), (1,⁻1)

4 isosceles trapezium (4,0), (4,6), (1,4)

Write one possible missing point for these shapes.

5 right-angled triangle (⁻5,⁻2), (⁻1,⁻4)

6 isosceles triangle (3,5), (2,1)

7 isosceles triangle (2,⁻1), (2,⁻5)

8 right-angled isosceles triangle (⁻3,1), (0,4)

Write the letter and coordinates of these points.

9 the coordinate total is 2

10 both coordinates are negative

11 the vertical coordinate is double the horizontal coordinate

12 the difference between the coordinates is 5

13 one coordinate is the inverse of the other

14 the product of the coordinates is 12

15 it is a reflection of (5,1) in the y-axis

16 it is a reflection of (1,3) in the x-axis

These sets of coordinates make five pairs of congruent triangles. Write the letters which match each congruent pair.

A (⁻5,⁻2), (⁻5,⁻6), (⁻3,⁻6)

B (1,3), (4,3), (3,⁻1)

C (4,⁻1), (6,1), (6,4)

D (0,2), (⁻3,3), (⁻1,5)

E (⁻6, 0), (⁻6,⁻3), (⁻4,2)

F (⁻3,⁻3), (⁻6,⁻4), (⁻4,⁻6)

G (1,⁻1), (1,⁻4), (⁻3,⁻2)

H (1,4), (3,6), (6,6)

I (3,⁻4), (1,⁻6), (⁻3,⁻6)

J (2,⁻6), (6,⁻6), (6,⁻4)

Drawing reflections

Copy each object and mirror line. Reflect each shape in the mirror line and draw its image.

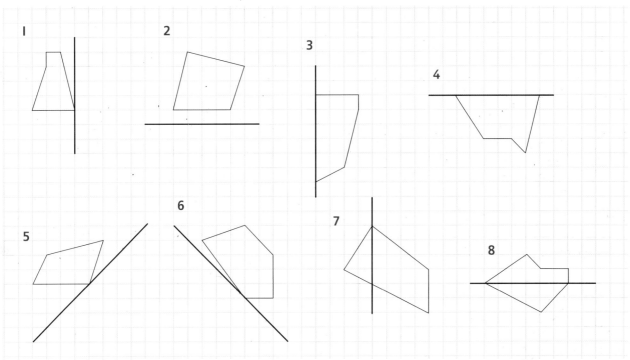

1

2

3

4

5

6

7

8

Copy these mirror lines. Draw one shape for each with these lines of symmetry.

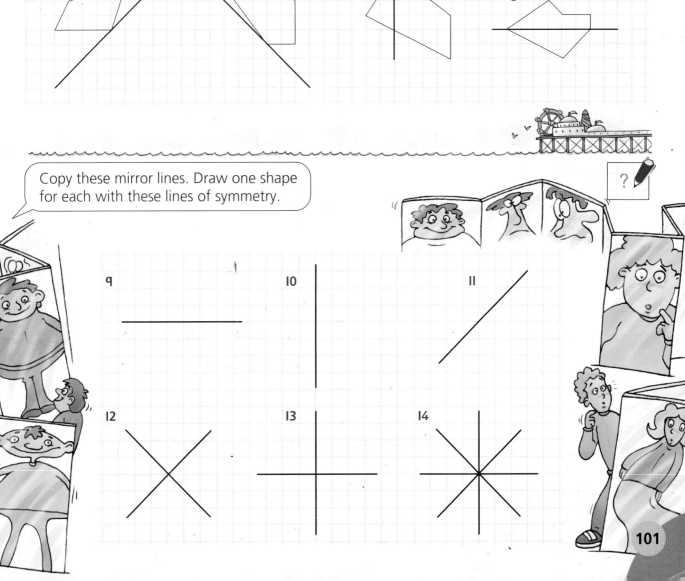

9

10

11

12

13

14

Drawing reflections

> Copy each word and mirror line.
> Draw the reflections of the words.

1. S I X | X I S

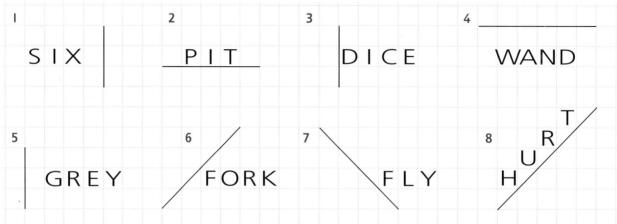

1. S I X
2. P I T
3. D I C E
4. WAND
5. GREY
6. FORK
7. FLY
8. H U R T

> Draw coordinate grids, and copy each shape.
> Draw the reflection of each in these axes.

x-axis   **y-axis**   ?

one axis, then the other

9.

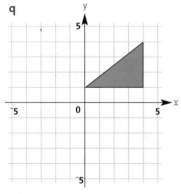

10.

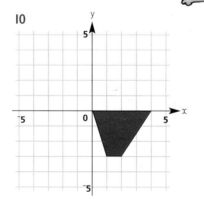

11.

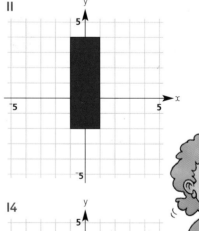

12.

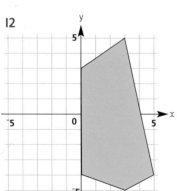

13.

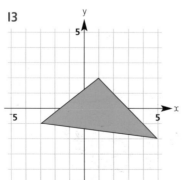

14.

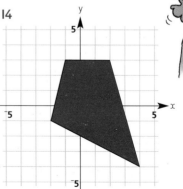

Rotating shapes

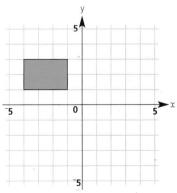

Copy each shape and draw its image after the given rotations about C.

1 C

90° anticlockwise

2 C

180°

3

C 90° clockwise

4 C

270° clockwise

5

C

90° anticlockwise

6 C

180°

7 C

270° anticlockwise

8

C

270° clockwise

Copy the pairs of triangles and images. Mark the centre of rotation, C, for each pair. Describe each rotation.

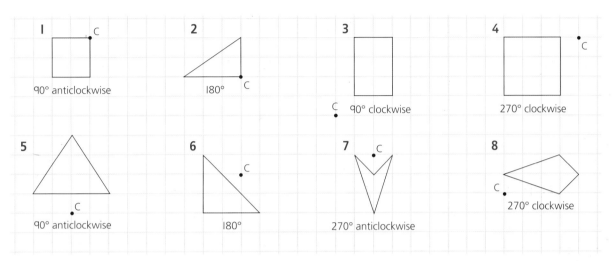

9 **10** **11** **12** **13**

Draw the position of the rectangle after these rotations.

14 90°, clockwise about (⁻1,3)

15 90°, anticlockwise about (0,0)

16 180°, about (⁻1,0)

17 270°, anticlockwise about (1,1)

18 270°, clockwise about (0,⁻1)

Rotations, reflections, transformations

Describe each transformation in one move only.

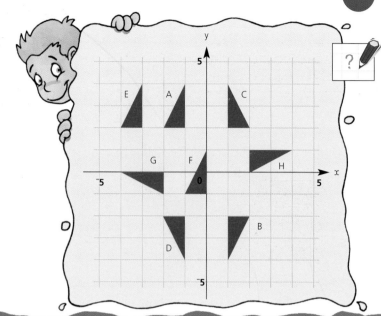

I	A to B	2	C to H
3	B to D	4	E to C
5	F to A	6	B to C
7	E to F	8	D to C
9	D to A	10	F to B

Write the coordinates of these points after each transformation.

11

reflection in the x-axis, then translation 3 up, 2 right

a   (3,2)

b   (⁻1,4)

c   (⁻3,⁻2)

12

translation 4 right, 1 down, then reflection in the y-axis

a   (2,⁻1)

b   (1,⁻6)

c   (⁻3,4)

13

rotation 180° about (0,0), then reflection in the x-axis

a   (⁻1,⁻4)

b   (5,⁻2)

c   (⁻1,0)

Draw the position of the triangle after these combined transformations.

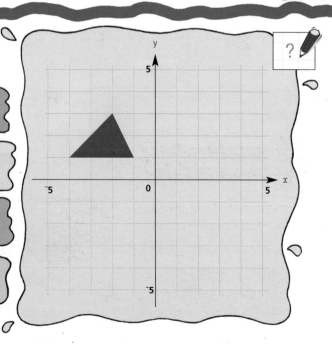

14 translation 4 right, 2 up, reflection in the x-axis, rotation 180° about (0,0)

15 rotation 90° clockwise about (⁻4,1), reflection in the y-axis, translation 4 left, 5 up

16 reflection in line y = ⁻1, rotation 90° clockwise about (⁻1,⁻3), translation 2 up, 1 right

17 reflection in x = 1, translation 3 left, 2 down, rotation 90° clockwise about (0,0)

Order of rotational symmetry

Write the order of rotational symmetry for each shape.

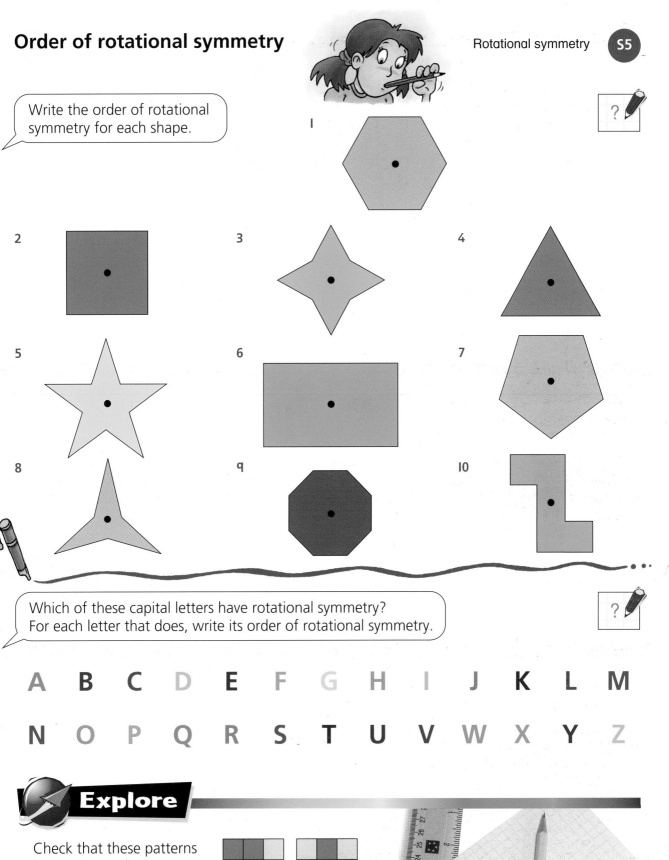

1

2

3

4

5

6

7

8

9

10

Which of these capital letters have rotational symmetry?
For each letter that does, write its order of rotational symmetry.

A B C D E F G H I J K L M

N O P Q R S T U V W X Y Z

Explore

Check that these patterns have rotational symmetry.

Draw some more patterns on a 3 × 3 grid.

How many can you draw that have rotational symmetry?

Line symmetry and rotational symmetry

Write which of these shapes have:

1 line symmetry and rotational symmetry

2 line symmetry, but not rotational symmetry

3 rotational symmetry, but not line symmetry

A   B   C   D

E   F   G 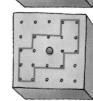   H

I   J   K   L

Explore

Use a 3 × 3 geoboard (or spotty paper).

Investigate how many different shapes you can create which have rotational symmetry.

Repeat for a 4 × 4 geoboard.

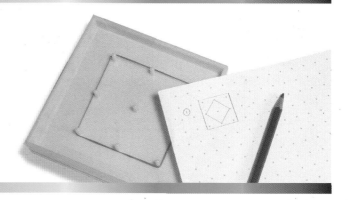

Explore

To create a shape with rotational symmetry:
- draw any shape
- mark a centre of rotation on one of its sides
- draw the image after a clockwise rotation of 90°, 180°, and 270°
- combine the shape and its three images to produce a shape which has rotational symmetry of order 4.

Create a set of shapes using this method.

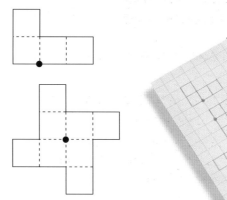

Views of 3-d shapes

For each of these shapes, draw a front view, a left side view, a right side view and a top view.

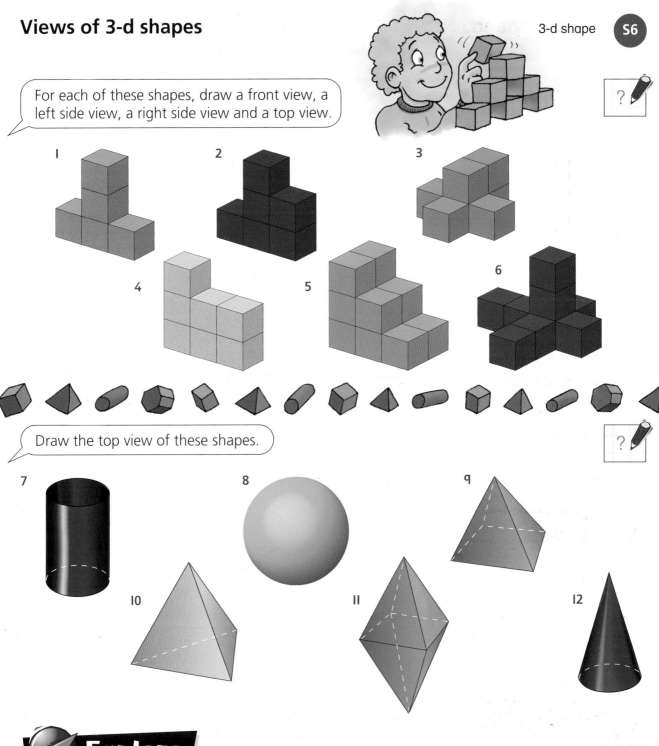

1

2

3

4

5

6

Draw the top view of these shapes.

7

8

9

10

11

12

Explore

Make as many different shapes as you can using 4 cubes.

How many different (non-congruent) shapes can you create?

Choose five of your shapes and draw the front, back, left side, right side and top views of each.

107

Views of 3-d shapes

For each of these shapes, draw a front view, left side view, right side view and top view.

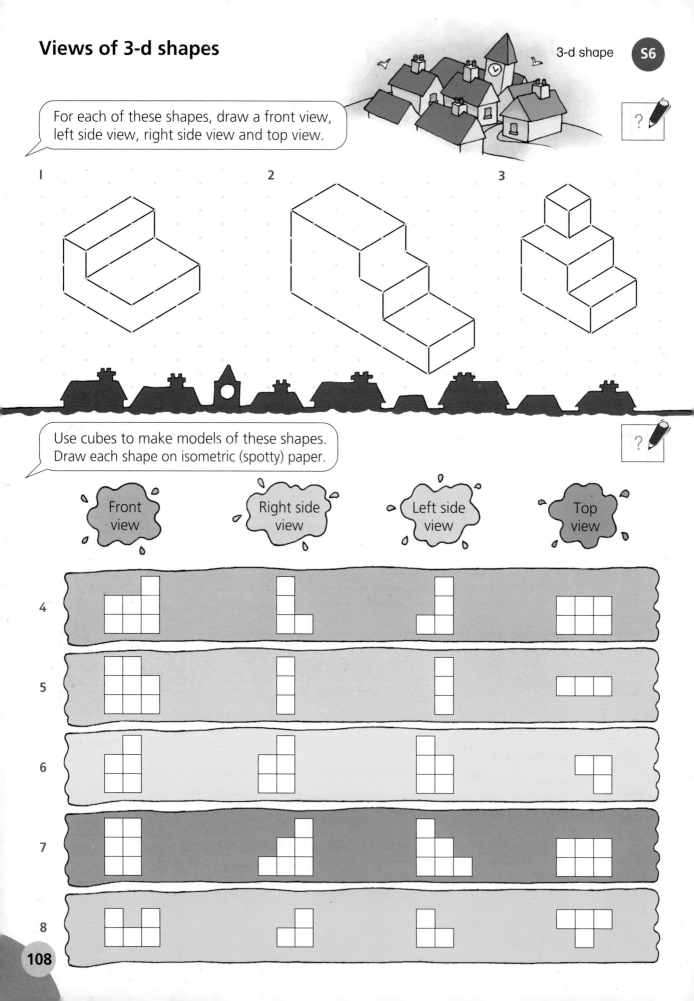

1

2

3

Use cubes to make models of these shapes.
Draw each shape on isometric (spotty) paper.

| Front view | Right side view | Left side view | Top view |

4

5

6

7

8

Congruent shapes

Copy each shape, then draw two more shapes which are congruent to it.

I

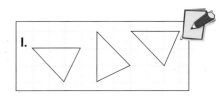

2

3

4

5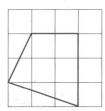

6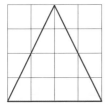

7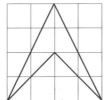

8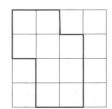

q

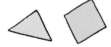

Draw a shape which has:

10 four sides, two right angles and two non-right angles

II one reflex angle, one obtuse angle, one acute angle and one right angle

12 four sides, one reflex angle and three acute angles

13 three equal sides all half the length of the fourth side

14 two obtuse angles, two right angles and two acute angles

15 three sets of parallel sides and all the sides the same length

Explore

Use a 3 × 3 geoboard.

Make 8 different triangles. There must be no congruent pairs.

Make 16 different quadrilaterals.

Investigate how many of your 24 shapes have:

a symmetry
b right angles
c parallel sides
d a reflex angle
e an obtuse angle
f equal angles

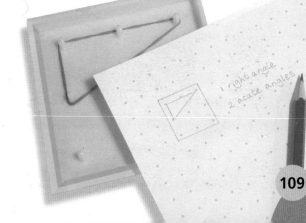

Write the name of each of these shapes.

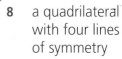

1 a triangle with one axis of symmetry

2 a triangle with three equal sides

3 a quadrilateral with four equal sides and no right angles

4 a polygon with equal sides and equal angles

5 a quadrilateral with equal diagonals

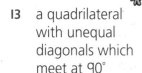

6 a triangle with two equal sides

7 a quadrilateral with two pairs of parallel sides, the lengths of which are not all equal

8 a quadrilateral with four lines of symmetry

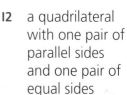

9 a triangle with two acute angles which are equal and one right angle

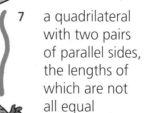

10 a quadrilateral with four right angles and two pairs of equal sides

11 a pentagon with equal angles and equal sides

12 a quadrilateral with one pair of parallel sides and one pair of equal sides

13 a quadrilateral with unequal diagonals which meet at 90°

14 a triangle with all sides of different length

15 a quadrilateral with two pairs of equal adjacent sides, an axis of symmetry and one reflex angle

16 a quadrilateral with equal diagonals and no right angles

Explore

Draw shapes on squared paper to investigate their diagonal properties.

Complete the table with these symbols.

✔ always

✘ never

? sometimes

quadrilateral	diagonals are equal in length	diagonals meet at their mid-points	diagonals meet at right angles
square			
rectangle			
parallelogram			
rhombus			
kite			
arrowhead			
trapezium			

Constructing triangles

Draw these triangles accurately, using a ruler and protractor. Measure and write the labelled sides and angles.

1
6 cm
a
60°
8 cm

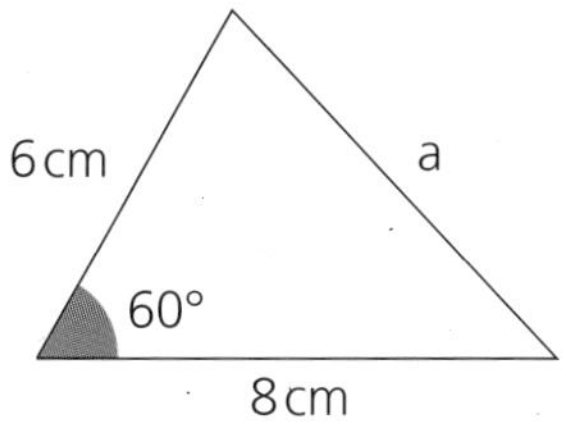

2
8·5 cm
85°
7 cm
b

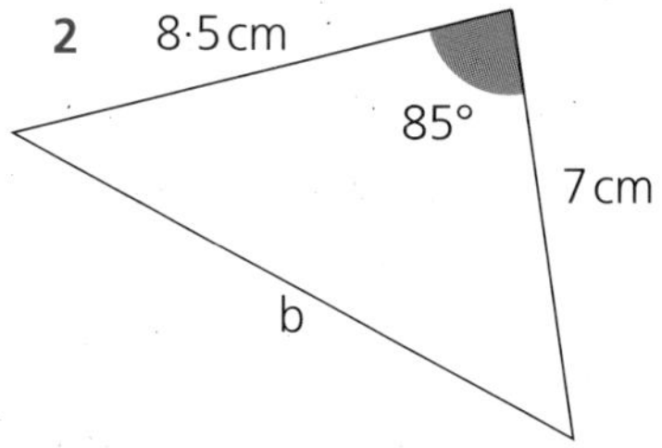

3
6·5 cm
c
72°
6·5 cm

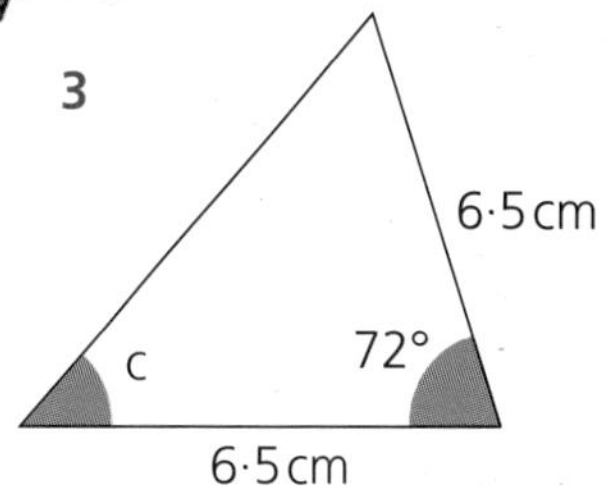

4 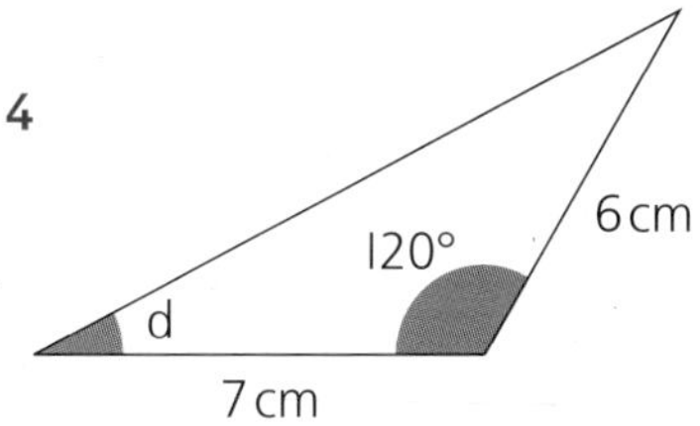
120°
6 cm
d
7 cm

5 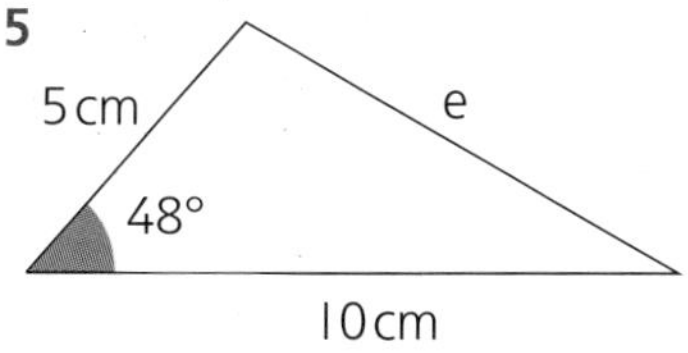
5 cm
e
48°
10 cm

6
f
5·6 cm
62°
11 cm

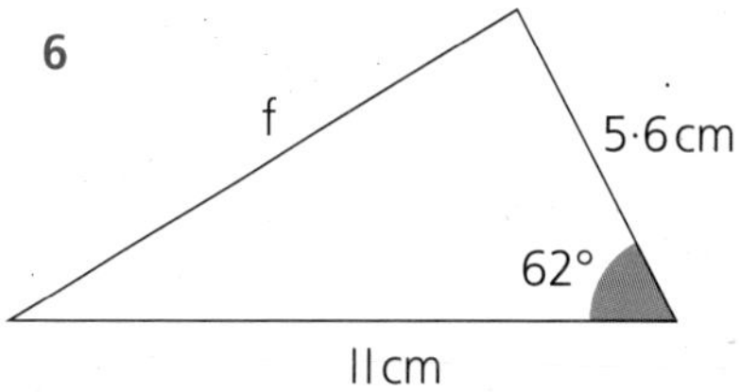

Draw these triangles accurately, using a ruler and protractor. Measure and write the missing sides and angles.

7
g
h
60°
40°
6 cm

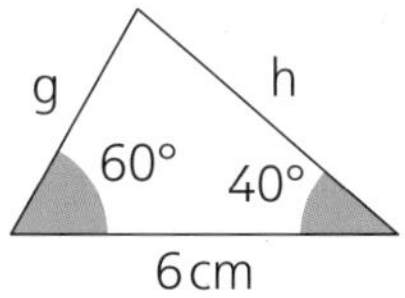

8
5 cm
85°
75°
i
j

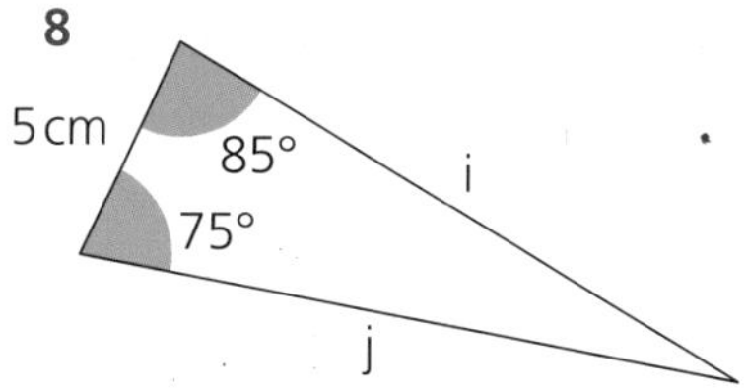

9
8 cm
40°
100°
k
l

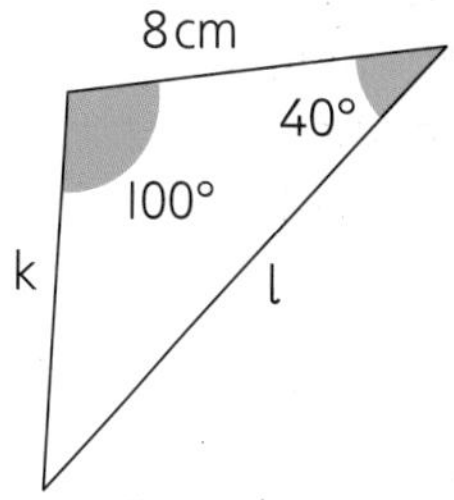

10
6·4 cm
68°
56°
m
n

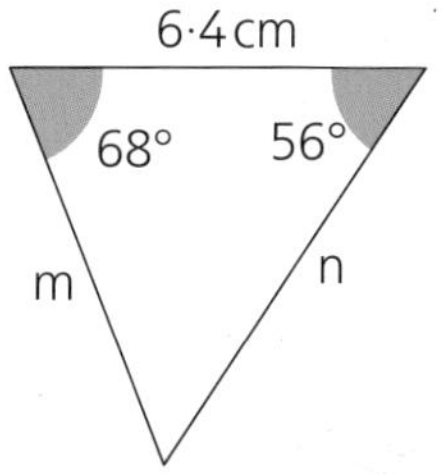

11
o
32°
125°
p
7·1 cm

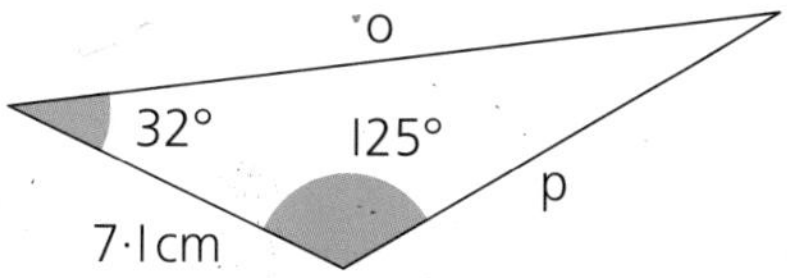

12
q
37°
98°
5·8 cm
r

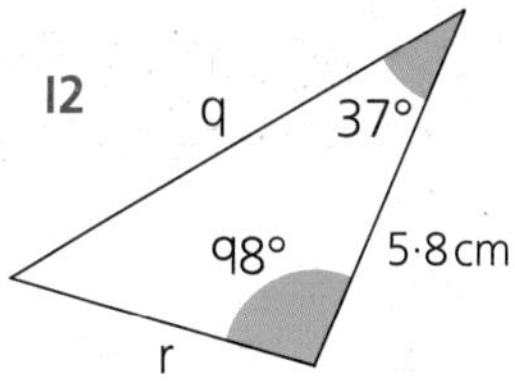

Explore

Construct right-angled triangles with these pairs of short sides.

For each triangle, measure accurately the length of the longest side. What do you notice?

Measure the angles of each triangle. What do you notice?

3 cm and 4 cm

6 cm and 8 cm

9 cm and 12 cm

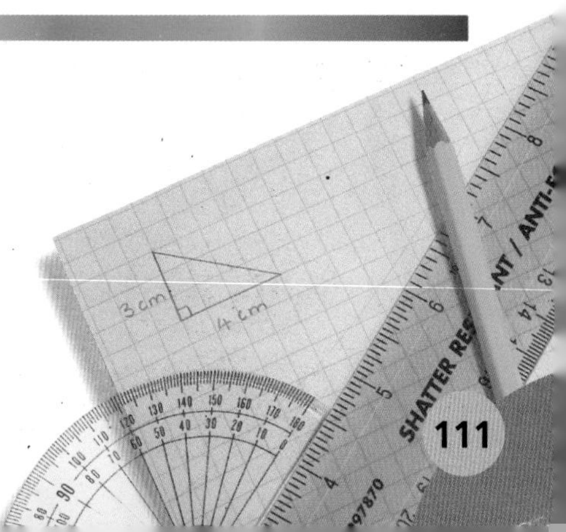

3 cm   4 cm

Constructing triangles and quadrilaterals

> Construct each triangle accurately.

1　equilateral triangle, side 8·3 cm

2　isosceles triangle, base 6 cm, base angle 75°

3　isosceles right-angled triangle, long side 10 cm

4　isosceles right-angled triangle, short side 6 cm

> Construct each quadrilateral accurately. Check the sizes of the other angles with a protractor.

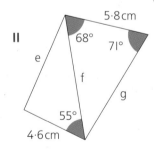

5　rhombus, side 7 cm, acute angle 60°

6　rhombus, side 8 cm, obtuse angle 110°

7　parallelogram, sides 6 cm and 8 cm, acute angle 72°

8　parallelogram, sides 6·8 cm and 9·1 cm, obtuse angle 114°

> Construct these quadrilaterals. Measure the lengths of the missing sides.

9
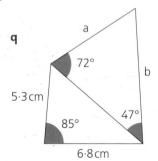
a
72°
b
5·3 cm
85°
47°
6·8 cm

10
c
58°
d
62°
7 cm
124°
6·3 cm

11
5·8 cm
68°
71°
e
f
g
55°
4·6 cm

Explore

Construct this kite.

Construct your own kite, first drawing a sketch with measurements.

Construct an arrowhead. You will need to calculate some more angles.

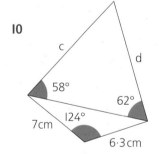
5 cm
80°
40°
8 cm

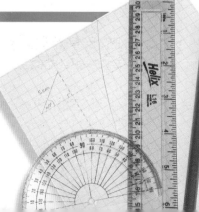

The data shows the recorded speed of the ten fastest mammals. Construct a graph to represent the data.

Find the approximate fastest speed of a human by researching the time taken for an athlete to run a mile.

Add the human's speed to your graph. Write some comments about what the graph shows.

Animal	km/h	mph
Cheetah	104	65
Pronghorn antelope	88	55
Mongolian gazelle	80	50
Springbok	80	50
Thompson's gazelle	75	47
Grant's gazelle	75	47
Brown hare	72	45
Horse	69	43
Red deer	67	42
Greyhound dog	67	42

The data shows the number of films shown on five television channels over four days. It also shows the year each film was released.

	29 May	30 May	31 May	I June
BBC I	1976		1994	1993, 1992
BBC 2	1937	1941		1948
ITV		1961	1963	
Channel 4	1964	1959, 1971	1957	1958, 1995, 1996
Channel 5	1966, 1998	1977, 1998	1994	1945, 1996, 1964

Construct a compound bar chart to show the number of films shown each day on both the BBC channels (I and 2) and the commercial channels (ITV, Channel 4, Channel 5).

Construct a pie chart to show the age of the films shown on all channels. Use categories such as 'up to 10 years old', '10–20 years old', ... or '1930s', '1940s', ...

Write what each graph tells you.

 Explore

Collect your own data about films on television this week.

Represent it graphically in different ways.

Representing data

The data shows the results of eight children in a memory test to remember words.

Construct graphs to compare:

1 boys' memory v girls' memory

2 memory of 3-letter words v 5-letter words

3 memory of words written in red v green

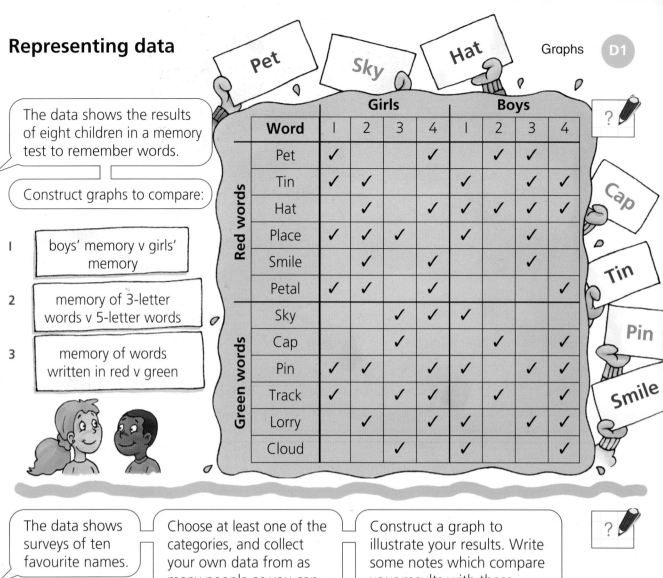

	Word	Girls				Boys			
		1	2	3	4	1	2	3	4
Red words	Pet	✓			✓		✓	✓	
	Tin	✓	✓			✓		✓	✓
	Hat		✓		✓	✓	✓	✓	✓
	Place	✓	✓	✓		✓		✓	
	Smile		✓		✓			✓	
	Petal	✓	✓		✓				✓
Green words	Sky			✓	✓	✓			
	Cap		✓				✓		✓
	Pin	✓	✓		✓	✓		✓	✓
	Track	✓		✓			✓		✓
	Lorry		✓		✓	✓		✓	✓
	Cloud			✓		✓			✓

The data shows surveys of ten favourite names.

Choose at least one of the categories, and collect your own data from as many people as you can.

Construct a graph to illustrate your results. Write some notes which compare your results with these.

Girls	Boys	Cats	Dogs
1 Alice	1 James	1 Sooty	1 Ben
2 Charlotte	2 Thomas	2 Tiger	2 Sam
3 Sophie	3 William	3 Smoky	3 Susie
4 Emma	4 Alexander	4 Tigger	4 Benji
5 Emily	5 Edward	5 Whisky	5 Max
6 Lucy	6 Charles	6 Kitty	6 Lucy
7 Katherine	7 Oliver	7 Lucky	7 Kim
8 Harriet	8 Nicholas	8 Suzie	8 Lady
9 Alexandra	9 Christopher	9 Fluffy	9 Shelley
10 Sarah	10 Henry	10 Snowy	10 Judy

Interpreting graphs

Use the pie charts to answer the questions about the ways children get to school.

How children get to school

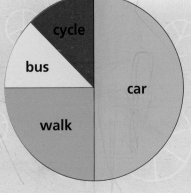

Junior School (480 pupils)　　　　**Infant School (300 pupils)**

1　Approximately how many children walk to the infant school?

2　Find the difference between the number of children driven to the infant school and the number of children driven to the junior school?

3　What percentage of all the children from both schools cycle to school?

4　How many more children take the bus to the junior school than to the infant school? Give one reason why you think more children get the bus to the junior school.

Use the graph to answer the questions about the amount of money collected in a sponsored walk.

5　How many children collected £20 or more?

6　How many children took part in the sponsored walk?

7　What fraction of the children collected less than £15?

8　Calculate the minimum and maximum amount of money that could have been raised.

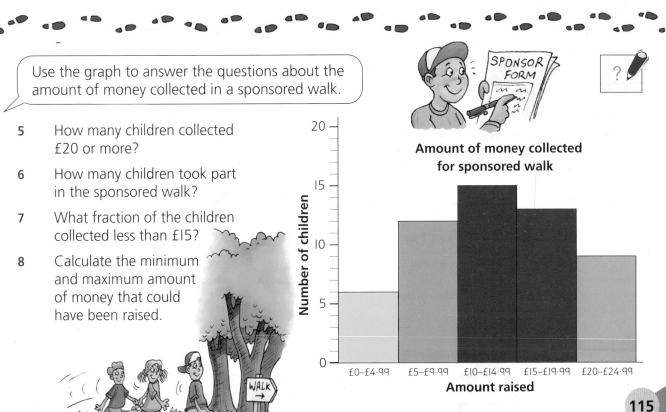

Amount of money collected for sponsored walk

Mean, median, mode

Calculate the mean, median and mode for each set of temperatures.

1
1°C 3°C 6°C
3°C 2°C 2°C 4°C
3°C 2°C 2°C 5°C
11°C 5°C

2
10°C
9°C 9°C
8°C 8°C
9°C 13°C
8°C 9°C 7°C
7°C

3
3°C
2°C 5°C
4°C 8°C
6°C 5°C 7°C
7°C

4
5°C
⁻1°C 6°C
2°C ⁻3°C
1°C ⁻1°C 1°C
⁻1°C ⁻4°C

The tables show the ages of the children who belong to each school club.

Copy each table, then draw a third column to help you find the mean age of the children in each club.

5

Football Club

age	children
8	4
9	3
10	6
11	3
12	4

6

Stamp Club

age	children
9	7
10	6
11	5
12	6
13	4
14	2

7

Dance Club

age	children
5	2
6	4
7	4
8	8
9	3
10	6
11	9
12	4

8 The mean age of five children is 11. If the ages of four of the children are 7, 13, 8 and 12, what is the age of the fifth child?

9 John scores 72 and 69 on two of his three tests. How many does he need to score on his third test to have a mean score of 65?

10 Six children have a mean age of 9. Their teacher, is 23 years old. What is the mean age of the teacher and children?

Problems

11 The mean of five consecutive numbers is 10. What is the mean of the first three of these numbers?

12 Nine children have a mean age of 8. Another person joins them. Together they have a mean age of 9·1. How old is the other person?

13 The mean of four consecutive numbers is 9·5. What is the fourth number?

Averages and spread

Calculate the mean and the range for the boys' marks and the girls' marks in each test.

Briefly write about each set of marks.

1 **Spelling test**

Boys	8	7	9	2	5	1	4	3	6	5
Girls	7	5	7	6	7	8	6	7	6	8

2 **Maths test**

Boys	5	6	5	6	6	7	6	7
Girls	10	3	4	9	5	2	8	7

3 **Memory test**

Boys	18	13	11	19	15	17
Girls	16	19	18	17	11	13

Calculate the mean of these sets of numbers.

4 the first six whole numbers

5 the first nine whole numbers

6 the first six consecutive even numbers

7 the first seven consecutive odd numbers

8 the first ten multiples of 3

9 the first six square numbers

10 the first five cubic numbers

11 the first six triangular numbers

12 the first ten prime numbers

Explore

These cards have a mean score of 6.

Write other pairs of cards which have a mean score of 6.

Write sets of 3 cards, 4 cards, 5 cards, and so on, that have a mean score of 6.

Averages problems

1 A cricketer scores 26 runs, 34 runs, 56 runs and a duck (0 runs) in 4 matches. What is his average score?

2 A football team has an average score of four goals over five matches. If they scored 3, 4, 1 and 5 in the first four matches, how many did they score in the fifth match?

3 The mean height of a group of six friends is 150 cm. The heights of five of the friends are 140 cm, 160 cm, 145 cm, 155 cm and 157 cm. What is the height of the sixth friend?

4 Over five weeks the scores in spelling tests of two friends are recorded.

| Sam | 15 | 14 | 9 | 10 | 17 |
| Jamie | 12 | 13 | 13 | 11 | 11 |

Who do you think is better at spelling? Explain your answer.

5 The heights of children in a class have a range of 37 cm. If the tallest child is 162 cm tall, how tall is the smallest child?

6 A group of people are travelling on a bus. Their ages are 12, 13, 14, 12, 14, 14 and 33. Would you use the mode, median or mean to describe their average age? Explain your answer.

A football team has a choice of shirts, shorts and socks, each in two different colours, to wear as their kit.

1

shirts   shorts   socks

Describe the eight different sets of kit the team could wear to play the next match.

Selina is making sandwiches. She has brown and white bread and three types of filling.

2

bread

brown   white

filling

cheese   chicken   egg

How many different sandwiches can Selina make with one filling in each? List them.

Jeremy has cubes in two different colours.

How many different towers of two cubes can he build? How many different towers of three cubes?

If Jeremy has cubes in three different colours, find out how many towers of three cubes he can build.

3

Explore

The Arrows, Bulldogs, Cougars and Dragons are four teams taking part in a competition.

Each team has to play each other team once.

How many matches are played in the competition? Write the teams in each match.

Investigate the number of matches played in competitions with five teams, six teams, and so on.

Probability

Two dice are thrown and the total score is found. Copy and complete the grid to show all the possible outcomes.

1

Green

	1	2	3	4	5	6
1						
2			5			
3						
4	5					
5					10	
6						

Red

Copy and complete the table to show the probability of each total.

2

Event	Chance	Probability
total is 2	1 in 36	$\frac{1}{36}$
total is 3		
total is 4		

How many times does each number appear on the grid?

Throw two dice 36 times. Compare the results with the probabilities in the table above. Write the results in a new table.

3

Event	Prediction	Result
total is 2	1	
total is 3		

Two coins are tossed to see if they land 'heads' or 'tails'. Copy and complete the table to show all the possible outcomes.

4

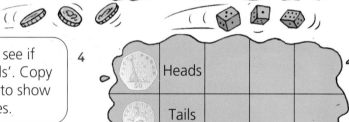

	Heads			
	Tails			

Copy and complete the table to show the probability of each outcome.

5

Event	Chance	Probability
both heads		
both tails		
one head and one tail		

Toss two coins 24 times. Compare the results with the probabilities in the table above. Write the new results in a table.

6

Event	Prediction	Result
both heads		
both tails		
one head and one tail		

Probability problems

1 A 1 to 8 spinner is used for playing a game. What is the probability of spinning:

   a a 5?

   b an odd number?

   c a number less than 3?

2 This spinner is used in a game. What is the probability of spinning:

   a a 5?

   b an odd number?

   c a number less than 3?

 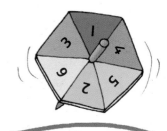

3 In a bag there are ten sweets. There are three toffees, two nut centres and five soft centres. What is the probability of:

   a picking a nut centre?

   b not picking a toffee?

   c picking a nut centre or a soft centre?

4 These raffle tickets are placed in a bag. What is the probability of picking:

   a an odd number?

   b a multiple of 5?

   c the number not being a 3-digit number?

5 On a 6-sided loaded dice the probability of throwing a 6 is $\frac{1}{3}$. How many sixes would you expect to throw in:

   a 30 throws?

   b 90 throws?

   c 108 throws?

 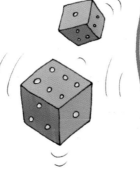

6 Jamie calculates that the probability of spinning a 3 on his spinner is $\frac{1}{5}$. How many threes would he expect to spin in:

   a 15 spins?

   b 45 spins?

   c 75 spins?

Mixed problems

1 A large cube is made from 27 small 1 cm^3 cubes. Find the surface area of the cube.

2 A tennis match lasts for 1 hour 54 minutes. In total 17 games are played. The players have a 90 second break after the first game and then after every two games. What is the mean length of game in minutes?

3 Diandra buys 3 colas and a hot dog for £2. Marli buys 2 hot dogs and a cola for £2·25. Find the cost of a hot dog and a cola.

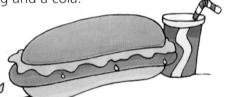

4 A phone call to Australia costs 65p per minute for the first 5 minutes and 34p for each minute after that. Kelly talks on the phone to her brother in Sydney for 13 minutes. How much does it cost her?

5 In a recipe 75 g of sugar is needed for every 120 g of flour. If 600 g of flour is used, how much sugar will be needed?

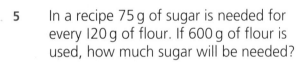

6 The time in Miami is 5 hours behind London. A flight to Miami takes 8 hours and 40 minutes. If the flight leaves at 4:30 p.m. local time from London, what is the local time in Miami when it arrives?

7 A bag of 20 apples of equal weight weighed 2·5 kg when full. If seven apples have been eaten, what does the bag weigh now?

8 Sugar cubes come in boxes of 400 cubes. The cubes are piled 10 high and 5 deep. How many cubes wide are they?

Mixed problems

1. Simon put £180 in the bank. The money earns 5% interest in the first year and another 5% interest on the total in the second year. How much money is in Simon's bank account by the end of the second year?

2. A shirt costs £17·50 in one shop with 20% off in the sale. The same shirt costs £18·40 in another shop, but has a 25% discount in the sale. In which shop is the shirt cheaper? Explain your answer.

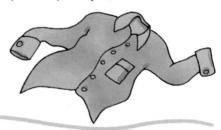

3. It costs 30p to park for 20 minutes on the High Street. Anita parks for 2 hours and 40 minutes. How much must she pay?

4. Marianne buys a burger for £2·60, a portion of chips for 75p and a drink for 95p. She does not eat in the restaurant, so she gets a 10% discount. How much does she pay?

5. A clothes shop offers a special deal – buy four items and get the cheapest one free. Martin chooses four things which cost £13·60, £15·99, £7·68 and £12·49. How much does he pay?

6. At the chemist's the deal of the day is three bottles of shampoo for the price of two. Three bottles would cost £5·55. How much does a customer pay with the deal of the day?

7. At the post office Dean buys 27 stamps. He spends £10·53 altogether. He buys nine 27p stamps. All the other stamps have the same value. What is the cost of one of the other stamps?

8. In his shopping bag Karl has 12 tins of soup. Each one weighs the same. The total weight of the bag is 4·5 kg. How much does one tin of soup weigh?

Mixed problems

1   I am a 2-digit multiple of 3.
I am an even number and
a square number.
Who am I?

2   I am a 2-digit number
greater than 70.
I am the product of
two prime numbers.
My two digits are the
same. Who am I?

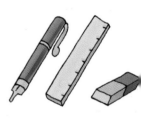

3   I am a 1-digit number. I am the product
of two consecutive prime numbers.
Who am I?

4   I am a factor of 36, 90 and
198. I am a multiple of 2, 3,
6 and 9. Who am I?

5   I am a 3-digit cube number.
The sum of my digits is 8.
I am not divisible by 5.
Who am I?

6   I am a 3-digit multiple of 10. I am the
product of two consecutive numbers.
I am divisible by 6 and 7. The sum of my
digits is 6. Who am I?

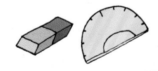

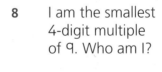

7   I am a 4-digit number. I am a multiple
of 100 and of 500. I am the square of
a multiple of 10.
Who am I?

8   I am the smallest
4-digit multiple
of 9. Who am I?

9   I am the square root
of a 3-digit number
between 200 and
300. I am a prime
number. Who am I?

10   I am the cube root of the
number which is 10
more than the difference
between the fifith
power of 3 and
the seventh power
of 2?

Mixed problems

1 There has been a 10% rise in Stephen's electricity bill. His bill is now £132. What was it before the rise?

2 Fiona has to buy a new carpet for her living room. The carpet costs £17 per square metre. If the room is 3 m wide and 4·5 m long, how much does the carpet cost?

3 A recipe for 4 people needs 180 g of sugar. How many grams of sugar are needed to make the recipe for 10 people?

4 A washing machine cycle takes 75 minutes and then the clothes need 80 minutes in the tumble dryer. The two machines can run at the same time, but clothes can't be put in the dryer until they have been washed. How long will it take to wash and dry 4 loads?

5 Mandy takes home a salary of £1200 per month. She spends £400 on her rent, £80 on gas and electricity, £120 on food, £35 on the telephone bill and £25 on water. What percentage of her salary does she have left over?

6 Marla needs new shelves in her bathroom. One shelf is 2·65m long, another 2·3m and the third 1·45m. A length of wood 3·8m long costs £7·35. The shelves need two brackets costing £2·69 each. How much will it cost Marla to put up her shelves?

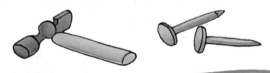

7 On Monday the milkman delivers two cartons of orange juice and a pint of milk for £2·75. On Tuesday he delivers one carton of orange juice and a pint of milk for £1·56. How much does it cost to have a pint of milk delivered?

8 A tin of paint holds 2·5 litres of paint. One tin contains enough paint to cover an area of 12 m^2 per litre. If the total surface area of his living room walls is 66 m^2, how many tins does Peter need to buy to paint his living room?

Mixed problems

1 Suzanne leaves the house at 07:20 to go to work. It takes her 20 minutes to walk to the station where she catches the 07:45 train. Her train is running 25 minutes late and the train journey lasts 40 minutes. How long does it take her to get to work?

2 The children in Year 6 are going on a school trip. The coach costs £256·80 which is shared between 48 children. They also need to pay £6·45 each for entrance to the theme park. How much will the trip cost each child altogether?

3 It costs Graham £32 to fill his car up with petrol. He travels an average of 240 miles on each tank of petrol. How many times will he need to fill his tank to travel 1500 miles? How much will it cost him?

4 The distance from London to Singapore is 6739 miles. A flight from London to Singapore takes 12 hours 45 minutes. Approximately how many miles an hour does the plane fly?

5 A group of 8 friends want to fly from London to New York. The air fare is £239 per person with a 15% reduction for groups of 6 or more. How much do the friends have to pay in total?

6 Sean travels to work 4 days a week by train. The return journey each day normally costs £6·80, but he buys a season ticket which lasts for 2 weeks and costs £50. How much money does he save over two weeks by buying the season ticket?

7 Three friends need to spend £42 between them on petrol to travel from London to Carlisle. If a fourth friend joins them, how much will each person save?

8 A one-way train ticket from London to Paris costs £49. A one-way ticket from Paris to London costs 423 francs. If there are 9 francs to the pound, is it cheaper to travel from London to Paris or Paris to London? Explain your answer.

Mixed problems

1 Two consecutive numbers have a product of 2256. What are the numbers?

2 Jenny is thinking of a number. She adds 7 to the number and multiplies the answer by 13. The answer she gets is 169. What number did she start with?

3 A cube has a surface area of 3456 cm^2. What is the length of one of the edges of the cube?

4 Continue this sequence by writing the next three terms. Explain how you would calculate the tenth term in the sequence. Explain the rule for the sequence.

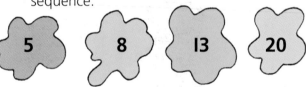

5 Sandy writes down the sequence '0·9, 1·2, 1·5, 1·8, 2·1'. He says, 'The eighth number will be a whole number and every tenth number after that will be a whole number.' Explain why he is right.

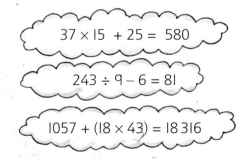

6 Sandra and Liz are playing a game. They roll two dice and score a point if they roll their target number. Sandra's target number is 7 and Liz's is 10. The first person to score 10 points wins. Sandra says, 'I think I am more likely to win'. Is she correct? Explain your answer.

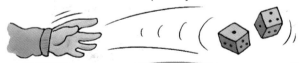

7 Decide which of these calculations are correct. Add any missing brackets.

$$37 \times 15 + 25 = 580$$

$$243 \div 9 - 6 = 81$$

$$1057 + (18 \times 43) = 18\,316$$

8 Copy and complete this calculation using prime numbers.

Mixed problems

1 Three 10-sided dice, each numbered 1 to 10, are rolled. The product of the three numbers is 48. Write all the possible combinations of the numbers shown on the three dice.

2 Darren is making sandwiches for a party. For every three sandwiches using white bread, he makes four using brown bread. If he makes 52 brown bread sandwiches, how many slices of white bread will he need?

3 A 3-digit number less than 500 is 1 more than a multiple of 3, 2 more than a cube number, and 6 more than a square number. What is the number?

4 It costs 5p per page to make a photocopy. If more than 100 pages are photocopied the price goes down to 3p per page for every page after the 100th page. If more than 300 pages are photocopied the price drops to 2p per page for every page after the 300th. Find the cost of 456 photocopies.

5 72 can be written as $2^3 \times 3^2$ as a product of primes. Find as many 3-digit numbers as you can that can be written as products of 2 and 3.

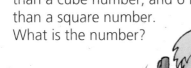

6 The square number 9 can be written as 2 + 7. Find other square numbers up to 100 that can be written as the sum of two primes.

7 A book is 2·8 cm thick. It has 480 pages in it. The cover is made from card 2 mm thick. What is the thickness of each page?

8 For his birthday Michael is allowed to choose from two presents. He can have $\frac{4}{9}$ of £279 or $\frac{3}{8}$ of £300. Which should he choose and why?